Dicky Blood's
War

By
Geoff Blore

Dicky Bloods War
First Edition
Published by DreamStar Books, March 2003

Lasyard House
Underhill Street
Bridgnorth
Shropshire
WV16 4BB
Tel: 00 1746 761298
e-mail: dreamstar@jakarna.co.uk

Set in Book Antiqua

Printed and bound in Great Britain by Orphans Press Ltd.

Dicky Blood's War

About The Author

Geoff Blore was born in Manchester in 1930. His family moved in 1937 and settled in Birmingham.

Geoff left elementary school at the age of 14 as a wartime evacuee and started an engineering apprenticeship which he followed through to completion. Then he went on to serve in the RAF for five years and, on leaving, became self employed for 30 years. He is much travelled and has lived in Egypt, South Africa and Australia.

Always a great sports fan, he has a special interest in squash, athletics and marathons. Now retired, his hobbies are golf, cycling and, of course, writing.

Yoxall, 1941 *and the coming of* **The Plague!**

Considered to be the oldest village in England, originally carved out of the once-great forest of Needwood long ago in Saxon times, charted in the Domesday Book, linked to the Arden family, Shakespeare's mother and the Compleat Angler, Izaak Walton, **Yoxall** was the fundamental embodiment of agricultural tranquillity. It's gentle sombre pace of life. It's slow meandering streams casually wending their way to hitch a seaward lift with the big river in the Trent valley. It's gentlefolk going about their daily, well ordered, lives. The farm workers singing as they encouraged their animals along at a pace slightly quicker than stop, as they gathered wild flowers and berries for their loved ones. The farm workers, not the animals. All was as it had been for years and would be for many more years. That is, until the plague came. Well not the plague exactly. More of a rash really! But it itched so!

This rash broke out in the early years of World War 2 and was called 'vaccies'. No! not vaccinations!. Vaccies!. If it was possible to get a vaccination, or an inoculation for the prevention of 'vaccies', there would have been dawn queues at surgeries in every village in Britain and everyone would have got the needle. But there wasn't. They couldn't. So they had to lump it!

This book is dedicated to those people who, in the face of interminable difficulties, upheaval, shortages, resentments and stresses, dealt, on a day to day basis with containing, and eventually coming to terms with, and accepting the well scratched rash called 'vaccies'.

And here's why!

Their clothing was in a deplorable condition, some of the children being literally sewn into their ragged little garments. Except for a small number, the children were filthy, and in this district we have never seen so many verminous children, lacking any knowledge of clean and hygienic habits.

Town Children through Country Eyes 1940
by Margaret Bondfield, *Britain's first woman Cabinet minister.*

In January/February 1941, approximately 100 pasty-faced, bag-carrying, string-labelled, wide-eyed 'Brummies', average age of 9 years, descended on Yoxall, a village of approximately 700 people. This is the true story of one of those 'little so and so's'.

This book is dedicated to the memory of all those people in Yoxall
and elsewhere who provided shelter, succour, guidance
and a different way of life to almost 2 million evacuated children of
World War Two, 1939-1945

Acknowledgements

I am especially grateful to Liz Guy, my Yoxall link, local searcher, organiser and arranger of meetings with local people with relevant information. Without her invaluable assistance, enthusiasm and encouragement, I doubt this book would have got finished.

I am also grateful to John Guy for his patience and kindness in allowing me complete freedom in and around the 'old mill'.

My special thanks to Jenny Lister, Priest in charge of St Peter's Church, for her wholesome support and 'delving' into school records, kindly provided by Mrs Jones, Head of St Peter's School.

To Helen & Colin Lester and Roger House, for all the information about 'Pop' Lester.

To Beryl & Syd Smith, Betty Housecroft, Mary Beddow, E.J.& J.T. Cooper, Joe Bamford, Kathy Bucknall, Mike Cuttle, Rose Sharratt, May Rowley and to the children of St Peter's School for 'hot seating' me.

To Mark of books4publishing.com for his enthusiastic professional guidance.

To my family, especially my sister Rita, for 'kick-starting' me in Australia and typing my early 'scribbling'. My daughter Emma, for her editing and her instruction/bullying in the use of a word processor. My son Steve, for his grammatical advice and finally, to my wife Jenny, for providing unlimited succour, enthusiasm and being a 'bouncing board' to my suggestions, ideas and strategies.

If I have forgotten anyone, I am truly sorry. It is however, undeniable proof that my short term memory is completely addled.

Foreword

Professor Carl Chinn MBE

It is almost inconceivable today for any mom or dad to contemplate letting your children, perhaps as young as six or seven, be taken away from you, to be put on a train or a coach, and then to be lined up in a church or village hall to be chosen by strangers to go and live with them. No matter how desperate the situation, very few of us would have any truck with any officials who demanded that we do such a thing. But that is what happened in the late summer and early autumn of 1939, and again in 1941, for tens of thousands of children from big cities like Birmingham, Manchester and London.

And let us be clear. The situation was not only desperate but also it was a time when authority held sway and when working-class and lower middle-class people were not prone to challenge officialdom. Fearful of a terrible loss of life because of enemy bombing raids, national and local government implemented a policy of mass evacuation of children from areas that might be bombed so soon as ever war with Germany was certain. Affected deeply by the Luftwaffe's bombing of Guernica in the Basque Country in the Spanish Civil War and by projections about loss of life from aerial attacks, it was believed critical to evacuate as many as children as possible from major industrial centres.

Some of those youngsters went with their moms, but the great majority were separated from their parents. They traipsed to school on the day of evacuation, clasping hold of a few belongings in some luggage and with their names indicated on pieces of card attached to strings and hung around their necks. Everywhere moms commanded older brothers and sisters to 'mind the babby! Don't you dare let go of her hand and you mek sure that you stick together and don't get split up!'

What a heart-rending scene it must have been as parents waved taraa to their kids at the school, wondering whether they would ever see their youngsters again. Concern creased into their faces and care caught in their eyes, they thought they were doing the right thing and sending their children to safety. Not all youngsters went, though, and many returned home during the Phoney War period, in time for the Blitz, which began in August 1940. Others were billeted with good people who cared for them and with whom they stayed for several years, whilst some had miserable times with uncaring foster parents.

And what of the feelings of the children who were evacuated? What thoughts raced through their mind, what emotions coursed through their being as they left with their tummies rolling with colly wobbles? And what of the experiences of the evacuees, their impressions of their new life, their longing of home, their excitement and apprehension? That is the great historical importance of this work. Geoff has brought to life the experiences of one evacuee and in so doing he has brought to the fore the lives and times of thousands more. This is indeed history written by one of those who lived through it.

Contents

Introduction

"What did you do in the war daddy?" The voice was piercing, demanding immediate attention.

Richard Blood looked up from the newspaper he was reading, to see his seven year old daughter Emma standing there, teetering on one leg, her other foot held by her hand up behind her back and her free hand using the nearby table as a support.

"Mmm, she's probably a stork this morning" surmised Richard to himself, not at all surprised by her pose. Emma was an imaginative, lively, inquisitive bundle of everything that makes a girl of her age such a joy. What did surprise Richard, apart from her unusually quiet entrance to his study, was her question. Granted, it was that time of year again, Remembrance and the media did seem to be making a big issue of it this year. Emma though was a busy, busy child, very like her mother, not given much to television and reading, apart from a few children's favourites.

"Well! Dad! What did you do? Were you a soldier? Did you smoke then? Did you kill anybody? Did you have to wash all that mud off before tea?" Emma had now become an aggressively playful big kitten, down on all fours, her head on his knees, rocking side to side on her chin and smiling, like Alice's Cheshire cat. Richard half expected to see her head rise bodiless and hover before him grinning.

They were very close. Despite his work taking him away a lot, Richard was very aware of the father/daughter special arrangement. He had three older sons. They were special to him too. All different and all getting on with life along their chosen paths. When he could be, he was there for them all.

"Alright! Alright!" he said to the crocodile, now lying full length on the carpet, it's jaws tugging at the slipper dangling from his swinging foot. "I'll tell you". There was a joyful squeal and the crocodile quickly metamorphasised back to the big kitten, now expectantly quietly attentive, both arms folded across his knee, her chin resting on her hands, her large eyes intent on his face, waiting.

Richard Blood carefully closed and neatly folded the newspaper he had been reading. He wasn't a particularly fussy or tidy person, in fact he would be the first to admit to being fairly disorganised and impulsive. But, he did like a newspaper to be neat, tidy and in it's correct order of pages. A two-page cricket report should be continuous, not interrupted by pages of uninteresting scandal and it irked him considerably when it happened. Emma of course, knew this and aided and abetted by her mother, would make a great play of missorting and neatly folding the pages when the opportunity presented itself. Later, she would offer to help Richard to sort them out by laying the pages all over the floor and making helpful comments like 'look dad, 2 and 79, 4 and 77, 6 and 75. As the numbers on the left of the page go up, the numbers on the right of the page go down. Can I cut all the numbers off one day and see if you can read it better?'

Richard would fix her with a stone faced look and with his forefinger trace a path across his neck. 'Do that and I will have to cut your head off" he'd say. Emma would erupt with delight. The newspaper, of course, would be forgotten.

Richard Blood put the paper down, plumped up and adjusted the cushions behind his back and gave a long and contemplative sigh.

"Well", he began, "I wasn't in the first big war called the Great War, now known as World War 1. I was in the next big war, known as World War 2, but I wasn't a soldier or anything like that. I was only a few years older than you are now when it started. I was an evacuee."

Richard paused. The kitten shuffled its bottom, its gaze firmly fixed on its quarry.

"What's an evacuee Dad?"

Do you want to go to Canada?

"Richard! Do you want to go to Canada?" Mrs Blood's voice, the tone and pitch shaped and honed by years of coping, mostly on her own, with now five very lively boys, *pierced the valley*, but not Dicky's totally absorbed imagination, *and echoed through the rolling hills where the bandits, about 20 of them, were furiously galloping south, away from the small town bank they had just robbed, towards the safety of the border, oblivious of the trap ahead set by the Canadian Royal Mounted Police, waiting patiently out of sight.* At the given signal, a wave by Dicky's right arm, the red and white marbles rolled out from their place of cover, an upturned old upholstered footstool, spread out and encircled the ordinary green, blue, brown and white striped marbles, the 'baddies'. The swift moving hands of 10 year old Dicky Blood orchestrated the ambush, the culmination of another exciting episode in the uninterrupted, continuous struggle to maintain law and order in the vast, untamed new world. Dicky's accompanying 'yips' whistles and bugle noises further embellished the action, all taking place under the old solid dining room table on the linoleum prairie.

"RICHARD!" Again the voice rang out, this time a few pitches higher and with the note held a bit longer. "Do you want to go to Canada?"

Dorothy Blood knew exactly where Dicky was and what he was doing. She always seemed to know, even when Dicky and his elder brother Maurice, were up to no good elsewhere. 'Queen of the fairies, that's what I am' she'd yell, whilst walloping their backsides and legs with the dreaded wooden mixing spoon.

"I always know where you are and what you are getting up to, you little sods!"

What's more, she usually did and the boys and their pals, some of whom had felt the weight of her hand, readily agreed. 'Dynamite Dolly', Roy Lines called her, not to her face of course and Alf Lines, Roy's older brother once said, 'A few like Dolly Blood at the front line with their wooden spoons would have sorted Hitler out.'

'CANADA!' The message finally pierced Dicky's fantasy world. He was well used to the varying pitch and tone and normally ignored it as long as possible, usually until the sound of rapidly approaching footsteps galvanised him into action. 'CANADA.' The name itself was just magic, conjuring up an immediate picture of mountains, forests, snow, bears, wolves and of course his beloved Royal Mounted Police, the 'Mounties', his fertile imagination serviced by weekly visits to the 'flicks', the local cinema on Saturday afternoons.

"Mom" he yelled, his knees and feet scuffing the floor as he, almost maniacally, sought to clarify this amazing possibility. Marbles, baddies and goodies, now completely forgotten were rolling, unimpeded everywhere across the linoleum square, on which the table and chairs sat, like an island surrounded by a sea of brown painted floor-boards. If you couldn't afford a square of lino' for your rooms, you were considered poor. Some people up in Hall Green, where Dicky and Maurice used to go 'odd-jobbing' for pennies, had real carpets on the floor; the hall as well.

"And pick up those marbles" yelled Mrs Blood, "if I come in there and break my bloody neck, I'll tan your arse until you can't stand up".

When riled, Mrs Blood often shouted contradictions, which sometimes upset her even more, but being of natural good humour, usually quickly realised what she had just said and readily laughed, which was fortunate for those within her reach.

Dicky quickly gathered up the marbles and put them in their box, an old battered Oxo tin, square with a hinged lid, and raced into the kitchen where Mrs Blood was busy 'dollying' the huge weekly washing. She paused, her face wet with steam and sweat and red from her exertions. Mrs Blood didn't just 'dolly' the washing, with her it was more a fight; an almighty battle to knock, screw and squeeze every bit of dirt and stain out of whatever was in the copper gas-fired tub. God help any kid who fell into the tub while she was dollying and she was often heard to shout to her brood returning home from play, 'Christ Almighty! I'll ave to dolly you little sods clean.'

Her neighbour and admirer Mr Towler, usually standing outside his house watching the world go by, would shout 'eh up Dolly! Been at the blue bag again?' and laugh, as would Mrs Blood as she patted her hair and attempted to smooth her rumpled worn out frock.

"Go on George, be off with you".

Although naturally shy, she did love these harmless encounters, which did not happen often enough in her hardworking life.

She looked across the kitchen where Dicky was jumping up trying to reach the top of the doorway, at the side of which, on the wall, were the pencil marks registering his and Maurice's height. All his pals could reach the top of their doorways with a jump, which greatly upset him. It wasn't as if he lacked energy and ability. He could run faster, jump wider parts of the local river Cole and climb more difficult trees down the Dingles, than his pals. He just lacked height.

"Cut out to be a jockey, I reckon Bill". He'd heard that sort of comment made to his father more than once when up at the club where he and Maurice, his elder brother by two years, were sometimes taken out of Dolly Blood's way on a Sunday morning.

There, Dicky and Maurice would craftily help themselves to the lumps of bread, cheese and slices of onion, put out for the snooker players including, more often than not, their father, William Thomas Blood, founder-member of the Yardley Wood Social Club in Birmingham and who, over the years, had fulfilled various duties. Sometimes secretary, sometimes Master of Ceremonies, sometimes treasurer and, according to Dolly Blood when talking to friends, 'all-time bloody nuisance!'

"Christ!" Dolly Blood shouted at Dicky, "can't you keep still, just for two minutes?" She sat down on the old wooden stool which was never far from her side in the kitchen, or when in the garden hanging out the washing. Her varicose veins which traversed the backs of her legs like black and blue mountain ranges, were a constant painful reminder to rest as frequently as possible, not easy for a mother of five lively boys and with no regular income from a mainly absent father, a commission salesman, who fortunately, was now a reasonably healthy person, after many years of poor health in the early 30's when there was little or no income. She spoke again, partly through her apron with which she was wiping her sweaty red face.

"Would you like to live in Canada for about a year? Lots of kids are going so you won't be alone and you can take Douglas with you."

Dicky was aware of evacuation. It had been on newsreels, like Pathe Gazette, shown at cinemas frequently since 1939, the year the war started and it looked fun to him. It often showed queues of kids from the cities; their gasmasks in containers slung around their necks and name-tags pinned to their topcoats. All were usually well-dressed and waving goodbye to their equally well-dressed families. Maybe it was untrue, but to many people and not a few politicians, it seemed evident that the class system was operating, as normal, in favour of the privileged and wealthy and that somewhere along the line the millions of poor would be considered. Ironically, many of the wealthy families, who had left London as complete families to stay with relatives and friends in 1939, returned as a result of the 'phoney war' period of little activity and hastily removed themselves again when the bombing of Britain began in earnest.

"Yeah mom!" Dicky had no hesitation or concern.

At last, it was going to happen. He might even get a bed to himself and 7 year old Duggie was no problem. Dicky already looked after little Duggie most of the time and regularly looked after all three younger brothers when Mr and Mrs Blood went to the club on Saturday nights, taking Maurice with them to help Dolly Blood with the catering she prepared and served on that night. Sometimes Dicky would go instead and Maurice would take his turn minding the kids. For Dicky and Maurice, it was a big night out and the opportunity to meet up with children of other club members. After all, it was a 'social club' and just one of many that mushroomed in working class areas in the late 30's and early 40's.

"Yeah mom!"

Dicky was now grabbing at Mrs Blood's apron, jerking it to accentuate his words and undoubted interest.

"When do we go? Can I take my marbles? Is the school going?" As many private schools had gone very early on. "Do you know who we'll be living with? Can I go out and tell my pals?"

"Now just calm down a minute will you? Chrissake! Nothing has been decided yet and it might not happen. It's just that the government are asking for people to put forward their names for consideration."

"Oh!" Dicky gloomily replied. "It's not definite then."

Dicky went into the garden and threw stones in the direction of the Anderson air raid shelter,[1] which was erected about 12 metres

[1] Over 2 million Anderson shelters were erected in the back gardens of houses throughout Britain. The shelter consisted of 14 sheets of corrugated steel, some curved to form a shell 1.8m high, 1.4m wide and 2m long. *ref*; www.fortunecity.co.uk/meltingpot/oxford/330/shel/shl2.html

from the house. No one minded him throwing stones or anything else at the shelter, in fact Billy Blood once yelled at him to include plenty of earth, mud and turf, if he could scrounge any. Anything that would add extra protection.

Being grown up and a veteran of the first world war, Billy Blood was only too aware that a direct hit on an Anderson shelter would be curtains for any occupants, so any extra covering would, at the very least, make him feel better. The Anderson shelters were delivered in sections complete with fastenings. The responsibility for erection lay with the occupiers and most got put up, one way and another. The first job was to dig a rectangular pit at least 500mm deep. This required, apart from basic tools, muscle, and the Bloods' and their neighbours were fortunate enough to have the eager help of 'Jan,' a refugee who had the looks and deeply tanned figure of a Kirk Douglas look-alike. Never mind that hardly anyone knew or was aware of the real Kirk Douglas at that time, most would later agree the resemblance was there. All the women, young girls and boys were enamoured of him, for different reasons of course. His power packed muscular body, stripped to the waist. His steady rhythmic working of whatever tool, spade, pickaxe, shovel or rake. His ready grin and broken English. Jan was a revelation!

Most kids and many adults, especially womenfolk, had never seen a foreigner close up, so to speak. The older women wanted to mother him. The younger wives and girls just wanted to be near him, the closer the better, and the boys all wanted to be him. The men were a bit jealous of course, but hid it well behind jocular comments about him and various activities. Jan would always laugh and nod his blond wavy haired head

"ja! goot! very goot! I like," and chuckle away. Rationing might be a problem, but the womenfolk always made sure that Jan's stomach was regularly replenished.

The Bloods' shelter was erected and all the local families came round to inspect it. Mr Towler bent down and poked his head through the narrow entrance, taking care not to catch his head on the sharp edge of the metal surround.

"Jesus Christ!" he shouted. "There's more room in our lavatory! I'll never get all my family in one of these." He withdrew his head, a concerned look on his face. Jan tapped the side of the shelter with his shovel.

"Not worry," he said, now leaning on his shovel. "When bombs come, many peoples get in this, sure t'ing". Jan nodded his head. He wasn't smiling and for the first time looked sad and older. He'd survived German Blitzkriegs and knew what was coming.

"Come!" Jan picked up his pickaxe and shirt, "next shelter, ja!" Jan would only stop for refreshment. Every garden site was already marked out for him and his gang of ready helpers. Men, women and children were always at hand to help when necessary. Some men, either unfit or too old for active service, also those deemed essential for munitions production, were also quite able diggers etc. But no one was like Jan, the instant, in the flesh, technicoloured real hero for all the kids. The local families, once he'd finished the necessary digging, never saw Jan again. Some displaced people, like him, would go to special camps. Some would enlist in military units comprising of particular nationalities like the Polish Brigade. All wanted to kill Hitler.

The Blood's shelter would eventually be moved several times because of rising water from the clay soil the rows of houses were built on, an ongoing problem for many years for most of the houses themselves, until improved technology, found a cure many years later. Many families, like the Bloods,' would eventually erect the shelters inside the house, where, of course, they were a nuisance, except during one of the frequent air raids. There were several types of individual shelters that would accommodate a family when necessary, the most popular being the Morrison shelter, which was more robust, smaller, and only held 2 or 3 people. Not very comfortable, especially if there were infants encased in their Mickey Mouse look-alike gas protection containers, complete with hand operated pump providing the necessary air to breathe. Some people, those used to doing things for themselves, would make the interior tolerably comfortable by putting wooden slatted flooring on top of concrete, make and fit wooden bunk beds both sides for children, narrow and neat, the bunk beds not the children. The children were usually narrow, rarely neat. 'Don't you know there's a war on?' Fat people of any age were rarely seen.

Modern day people, especially youngsters, when seeing a Anderson shelter in a museum for the first time, will wonder how families, some with large numbers of children, coped with the 'all night raids' of 12 hours and more. Many shelters, in the gardens for the duration of the war, resembled grassy mounds, the shelter below protected by several feet of sandbags covered with earth and turf and remained so for many years to come, now doubling as extra storage for a variety of purposes. Private house owners and men, who earned more than £5 weekly, had to pay £7 for a family size shelter. Council tenants were provided with shelters, as were schools etc. The latter were usually brick and reinforced concrete and could hold upwards of 40 people. Any seating was fixed wooden along the sides and down the centre, two classes and two teachers to each shelter.

Temporary lighting had to be carried in as no services of any kind were provided. Toileting was an adventure and when necessary, supervised by a teacher complete with bucket and sometimes the two times table by the kids, with little ad-libs of course. It was rarely dull and in the early days of the war, air raid drills were a regular event. At the first sound of the warning siren, all the children would sling the container holding their gasmask over their shoulder and walk, supervised in class groups, to their nominated shelter, where they would put on their gasmasks, practice their arithmetic tables and sing songs, much to the joy of those boys who, with a little practice, could make rude sounds through the rubber side flaps of the face mask.

Anderson Type Shelters

A Near Miss

It was getting light and the 'all clear' siren hadn't sounded, even though it had been some time since the dull throbbing drone of the last German bomber planes had faded away, as had all other sounds of conflict. There was just an eerie silence, no bird song, no clatter of hooves signalling delivery of milk or bread, no engine noise of an early morning passing lorry or car and thankfully, no sound locally of fire engines or ambulances, which suggested Yardley Wood had again been lucky. The strange, all-pervading, silence almost hurt Dicky's ears as they strained to detect the slightest sound of imminent further mayhem. Still very fresh, in the air-raid occupant's reeling senses, were the long hours of screaming bombs preceding the earth shuddering explosions, shattering buildings and lives indiscriminately. The anti-aircraft batteries spitting their noisy defiance as they hurled skyward their salvos of high explosive shells, all primed to explode, hopefully in or near the German bombers, steadfastly and remorselessly, flying through the long fingered beams pushed up by the batteries of searchlights. The shattered remains of these shells (shrapnel) falling silently, like deadly rain, creating their own minor destructive sound as they shattered roof tiles and greenhouses alike. And all accompanied by the steady, engine throbbing, orchestra of hundreds of German bombers taking their turn to unleash their deadly payload.

The only sound now, was the occasional trickle of disturbed earth settling against the outside of the steel Anderson shelter. This familiar sound, now so unremarkable after so many nights in the shelter, was, I suppose, like someone near you breathing. Something to get used to and eventually not notice.

'So quiet,' Mr Towler would later exclaim, 'you could hear a frog fart!' This new expression, latched on to by 12 year old Maurice, senior entertainer and responsible when Mom and Dad were at Yardley Wood Social club, would be later used to good effect when days later he handed out pencils and paper to Dicky and Duggie, asking them write down all the names of animals they thought might blow off! Of course, it turned into a hilarious evening and the time passed more quickly, enabling Maurice to get the youngest two, three year old Barry and one year old Laurence, off to sleep and giving Dicky time to run round to the chip shop in Ravenshill Road for 'three pennorth' to share between them.

Another sound, much lower, pierced the silence. It was the rumbling of Dad's stomach, which was yelling out for sustenance.

"Sod this!" he muttered, "I'm going to get some bacon on, siren or no siren".

He climbed up out of the Anderson shelter and scurried the 20 yards to the house. In about 5 minutes flat, the remaining occupant's senses were assailed with the wonderful, succulent and enticing smell of frying bacon. After about 10 hours stuck in that tiny shelter, the family was really hungry. Sure, they'd experienced raids, more than enough, but not an 'all-nighter.' On those occasions when Dolly Blood was working nights and Billy Blood was 'on duty' at nearby Wythall Barrage Balloon Station, one of the elder Bentley sisters, Hilda or Lily, would sit with the Blood kids. Just as, later on, Evelyn and Joyce Bentley would look after young Barry and Laurence when needed. The Bentley family were neighbourly! In every sense of the word and much appreciated.

Most other raids had started late in the evening and were usually over a few hours later. This one had started early and although it was now quiet, no 'all clear' siren had sounded, so it had to be assumed that enemy aircraft were still about. Duggie, Barry and baby Laurence, were still asleep in the makeshift bunks that their Dad had 'rigged up' along one side of the shelter and along the back. This left room for two chairs for Dicky's parents to sit on, near the small shelter entrance, leaving just enough room for people to get in and out.

Maurice was all for going in to help his Dad, despite his Mom's insistence he stays where he is safe and to leave things to his Dad. The overpowering aroma was too much for Maurice though and he climbed out and made for the house and the sound of that lovely bacon sizzling. He'd only gone a few steps when that tantalising frying sound was suddenly drowned out by the terrific roar of a low, fast flying, plane's engines, the almost immediate sound of shattering glass, the clatter of a falling frying pan and the pained cursing of Billy Blood. Maurice had got back into the shelter a damn sight quicker than he'd got out, just a split second before his father's diving body tumbled in and crumpled in a cursing heap at Mom's feet. In the confines of the shelter and amid the sudden return of the deathly silence, Dolly Blood helped her husband up and said

"You've got blood on y'face. Did that plane drop somethin' that 'it you?"

"Some bleedin' thing came through the window", replied Billy, wiping the blood away with his hanky. "It landed on the kitchen floor and I didn't stop to find out what it was. I do know that the bacon is keeping it company and that they can both stay there, cos I ain't goin' back in".

He paused to look around and seeing the three youngest were still asleep, continued, "As for this blood, I reckon I got that when I dived in the shelter. Must 'ave caught me 'ead on the metal frame, or something."

He then settled back and after a few minutes said despondently, "I didn't even try, even just one tiny piece of that lovely bacon" and sighed.

Dolly Blood gave him a very old fashioned look, born of close acquaintance with a travelling, smooth talking, salesman, an occupation Billy Blood had followed for several years of his life. A few silent minutes passed before Mrs Blood noticed her husband's wet trouser leg.

"Ow y'got your leg wet like that then?" she asked.

Bill looked down to where he was subconsciously rubbing his shin in the wet area. He pulled up his trouser leg to reveal a red welt across the tattoo of Borneo, a memento of his seafaring days. He got up from his seat, looked out of the shelter towards the house, muttered a quiet obscenity and sat back down.

"Well!" Dolly said with a fair bit of irritation in her voice. Billy looked at her, a weak, resigned sort of grin on his face. "I must 'ave caught the piss bucket with my leg on the way in".

Air raid shelters didn't come provided with toilets, indeed there were many thousands of houses without flush toilets at that time. It was never a big problem though. If the bombing was local and severe, the bucket, which was always just outside the shelter entrance, was lifted in as required and lifted out after use.

Dolly giggled and remarked "could 'a bin worse," she giggled again, "could 'a bin a bit more than pee in it."

Bill shrugged his shoulders and wearily replied "not much different there then, I've bin in some sort of shite most of me life." His Lancashire accent, always more noticeable when he was excited or fed up, defeated and sent packing the carefully cultivated 'sales representative' patter he now used in his office job at The B.S.A.

About an hour later, the 'all clear' went and the family ventured back into the kitchen to find that the 'missile' was the tailfin of an incendiary bomb. Where the main part of the bomb landed, was never found out. Presumably, it hadn't exploded, which wasn't unusual. Dolly Blood rescued the bacon, checked it for broken glass, rinsed it under a running tap and finished frying it. It tasted marvellous!

Birmingham High Street, after an all night raid

Leaving Brum

February 1941

The German armies seemed to be advancing everywhere. There was lots of coverage on Pathe News, at the cinema, showing stiff British resistance and bravery, but Dicky and his pals, like lots of kids his age, were excitedly waiting for Jerry to land, maybe from the sky, as they were supposed to be brilliant storm paratroopers, or the more normal seaborne landings. It didn't matter much to Dicky and his pals, soon they would be caught up in the action and hopefully get some real battle souvenirs, much better than ordinary lumps of shrapnel from bursting shells and bombs during air raids. Danger wasn't considered.

Most kids below the age of 12 thought it was all very exciting, a bit of a nuisance regarding shortages of everything, but more exciting than the 'make believe' at the 'flicks'. The gang had discussed their plans several times. Billesley Common they judged the most likely place for German paratroopers to land. Jerry would surely want to capture the anti-aircraft batteries that kept knocking hell out of the Jerry bombers, or so they were led to believe by the confident tones of the English BBC Radio announcer the morning after a particularly bad raid. 'Heavy bombing by German planes (who else?) took place last night targeting several major cities. Some damage was sustained and light civilian casualties have been reported. The accurate anti-aircraft fire and superb skills of our night fighters soon drove off the enemy who sustained heavy losses.'

FACT - **2 million homes** would be blasted by German bombing raids on cities and provincial towns in the UK. **58,000 civilians would be killed**, with many more thousands injured. Many complete families would be wiped out overnight, **night after night**. No city or town was considered safe. These sort of facts though were never mentioned, no doubt by the order of Winston Churchill, undoubtedly the greatest war leader of all time and whose picture was everywhere, photo's, cartoons, comic strips and always the beaming smile and raised two fingered "V" for victory sign. Most kids, including Dicky, would play out war dramas in a variety of imaginative ways, some even involving cinema hero's like The Lone Ranger, Tarzan, Buck Rogers etc. The German's and the Italians were always the 'baddies'.

Dicky Blood and his young 7 year old brother Duggie, joined about 100 other kids who were waiting outside the school. All were fully dressed, with name tags pinned to their outer garments, gas masks slung over their shoulders and carrying what spare clothes and personal possessions they owned. Yardley Wood was mainly a Council estate housing working class people. Wives rarely worked for pay before the war. Many jobs involving women were to become available soon after the war started, mainly in factories. But early in the war, the man of the house was the breadwinner and his money did not stretch to fripperies, so most kids could easily put their few things in a small case or carrier bag. Many kids were volunteered for evacuation simply because their parents could not afford good quality food and, when it came, food rationing made it a fairer system for the poorer element in society.

The Ministry of Food was set up and advice on preparation of what foods were available were frequently published and broadcast by Lord Woolton, Minister of Food.

All those who could, grew vegetables and kept egg-laying hens. Schoolboys would go in organised gangs from school to these gardens where there wasn't a man in the household. All scraps were saved and given to those lucky enough to be able to keep a pig. The givers to be later rewarded with, perhaps, a couple of chops. Black marketing was soon rife, especially in London where most of the richest usually lived. SPIV became the nickname for the man who could get anything, for a price. Whilst many were being killed defending Britain, others were getting rich and making plans to get even wealthier after the war. The age of innocence, valour and honour was passing by.

Duggie Blood looked bewildered by it all. He was too young to understand really. Mrs Blood spit on her hanky and wiped his concerned little white face. He always looked hungry, whereas Dicky always felt hungry. He'd found a tanner (2.1/2P) once. He gave twelve year old Maurice, his older brother half and spent the rest on

6 iced buns, which he promptly ate, feeling full for probably the first time in his life. Maurice, being older and more responsible gave his 'half a sixpence' to his Mom, knowing she'd be short of money as usual and told her about Dicky. Another walloping with the wooden spoon.

Some of the shopkeepers were standing in a little group, but not too far from their shops opposite the school. One of the shop owners, Mr Hall, seeing that he had got Dicky's attention, pointed his forefinger to his bespectacled eyes, and then pointed it at Dicky who grinned delightedly and waved back. Dicky's mind went back to that hot summer day two and a half years ago... **'Thievin' little ***!'**

Dicky was making his way home from the local library. As he approached the block of local shops, Dicky remembered that his father had asked him to bring back a box of matches. He checked that the few coppers were still in his pocket, pushed the shop door open and entered. The bell over the entrance gave out it's usual, startled, ring, but no-one appeared. Dicky thought the owner, a Mr Hall, must be in the backyard and put his library book on the wooden counter. A few more seconds passed and Dicky, not for the first time, reached over the counter to where a variety of unwrapped sweets were displayed in open boxes. Closing his grubby fingers over a few sweets, he started to withdraw his hand when another, much bigger, hand suddenly appeared and firmly took hold of Dicky's wrist. Terrified and unable to move his limb in the grip of the rigid fist, the only other part of the owner visible being a thick hairy wrist, Dicky yelled out "let me go! I'll tell me Dad!"

"No! I'll tell your Dad!"

The voice was deep and menacing and Dicky was horrified when the rest of the arm slowly came into view, followed by the head and scowling face of Mr Hall.

"Got you! y' thievin' little sod!"

Still gripping the wrist of Dicky, whose eyes were starting to leak tears, Mr Hall moved into full view the other side of the counter.

He was not a big man but generally smart and usually wearing a dark suit. His general demeanour was frighteningly similar to that of Mr Spicknell, the fearsome headmaster of Yardley Wood School whose reputation had long ago filtered down to the junior boys like Dicky.

"So, what's this y'reading this week?" Mr Hall picked up Dicky's book. He obviously knew that Dicky was a regular library user. Still holding Dicky's wrist, he read out loud the title "William the Pirate by Richmal Compton." He flicked over a few pages, reading pieces here and there, sometimes to himself and sometimes out loud with a restrained chuckle. "About y'dad is it? He's a William isn't he! Bit of a chip off the old block are you? Was he a THIEF too? Will 'e be pleased when I tell 'im 'is little pride an' joy NICKS sweets?"

Mr Hall was getting angrier, shouting and losing the carefully 'middle class' accent that most retailers, of necessity, cultivated as respectable small business owners, now on a social par with teachers, dentists, hospital matrons and vicars, but not bank managers, town councillors, doctors or bishops.

He stopped shouting, released the terrified Dicky's wrist and continued, "Can I keep your book then? After all, you were trying to STEAL from me." Every time Mr Hall used the words thief, steal or pinch or nick, he would put great emphasis on them.

"You can't have the book," Dicky blurted out. "It belongs to the library."

Mr Hall smiled, a look of triumph on his features "Well you can easily STEAL one can't you? That's what you do isn't it?"

Dicky squirmed with embarrassment. The shopkeeper continued, "Do you want me to tell your dad?"

Dicky, now thoroughly chastened, red and wet-faced, muttered "No". He knew he'd get a telling off and a clip round the ear from Billy Blood. He also knew that his Mom would then find out and he would, most certainly, get a 'tanning' with the wooden mixing spoon on the back of his legs, his backside and also his hands, if he was daft enough to try and protect his bum with them.

Dolly Blood just could not tolerate any form of desecration of the 'ten commandments' and she classed thieving only marginally better than lying.

'You know where you are with a thief!"' she'd shout. 'But you never know where you are with a liar!' Dicky would never forget those sentiments, which would be proved right later on in his turbulent life.

Mr Hall, now at ease with himself, continued "Hmmn! Well, I can't have your book, but I do have to punish you in some way. Do you agree with that?"

Dicky nodded. He'd quite definitely be happier being punished by Mr Hall. His parents would then not know about the incident and he would certainly not pinch another thing in his life. Not ever! Ever! Again! He could feel the relief surging through his whole body.

"Yes! Can we get it over with now?" He'd picked up this strategy from his older brother Maurice several years before. Frequently in trouble together in a variety of escapades and knowing they were going to 'cop it' when they got home, Maurice would encourage Dicky to run home with him to 'get it over with'.

"How old are you?" Mr Hall asked, still holding the book.

"I'm eight and a half," replied Dicky eagerly. "I'm good at tidying up or washing up and I can peel potatoes. I don't mind".

Mr Hall, now enjoying the situation said, "If you don't mind? It's not much of a punishment is it? You might enjoy doing those sorts of things. Maybe you should pay me for letting you do them."

Dicky, somewhat mistakenly, thought he detected a softening in Mr Hall's attitude towards him. Now grinning, he said "No, I'll do it for nothing."

Mr Hall's glare immediately restored the balance. He came round the counter, opened the door to the back of the shop and, still holding the book, motioned Dicky through. Gripping the collar of Dicky's jersey, the shop-keeper ushered him through the storeroom and into the backyard. There he released Dicky, waved his arm around the yard and said "There's pop bottles need sorting and putting in their proper crates and the rest tidying up and swept clean. When you've done that you can go. I'm leaving this door open so I can keep an eye on you. I don't want anything else going astray."

Dicky did what was required in about twenty minutes or so, knocked the back door and shouted "Mr Hall, I've finished."

The shopkeeper came out, the open book in his hand, looked around the yard,

"Yes that'll do, which is a pity really. I was just getting into your book. I've never read any of the 'William' books."

Dicky saw his chance to make amends. "You can finish it if you want to. I can easily read it in two days. Just as long as I get it back to the library before two weeks are up."

Mr Hall looked at him for a while, then said "No! Take it! I'll get my own book from the library. I'm also a member."

He'd decided, probably quite rightly, not to accept a favour from someone who had tried to steal from him. Dicky, book in hand, quickly scuttled out of the shop and ran home, Mr Hall's shouted words chasing him 'I've got my eye on you, young Blood!'

His father, looking up from the daily paper he was reading, said "Another William book! Good! I think I enjoy them more than you do. Where's the matches?"

Dicky had completely forgotten about the box of matches but, for the rest of his life, he would never forget Mr Hall and the last time he tried to steal anything...

Dicky, subconciously rubbing his right wrist at the memory had his reverie interrupted by his mother's urgent voice.

"Now just you make sure you look after Douglas."

Mrs Blood was agitated. She felt she was doing the right thing. Her youngest boy Laurence was 18 months old and Barry was nearly 3. Her husband Bill was in the RAF and she was working nights at the Austin works, making armoured car parts. She would need Maurice, now almost 13, at home to look after the kids.

"Now don't forget, as soon as you get to where you are going to live, write the name and address of the people on that piece of paper in that envelope addressed home and post it."

Most of the kids were excitedly trying to board the buses, some mothers were crying, some kids were reluctant to leave. The teachers were being sensible and, well, being teachers.

"Come on now, you are going to lovely homes away from all these air-raids and black outs. You are all going to have fun and some of us are coming with you because we know it's going to be so nice."

Bryn Jones and his younger brother Michael were sitting near the front of the bus, Dicky and Duggie sat behind them. Dicky had got to know Bryn only a few weeks before and had been to his parent's house in Goodrest Croft where all the privately owned houses were smart with well kept gardens. Bryn always had new comics and would sometimes pass them onto Dicky who would read them and swap them on the council estate where he lived. Dicky had said his goodbyes to Joyce Bentley, his next-door girlfriend, also to his school girlfriend Eileen Scrannage, who liked to race Dicky up and down Yardley Wood school playground. He would have liked one of the girls as a sweetheart, but he didn't want to lose the friendship of either, so didn't declare himself either way. He said he would write to them both, but he didn't.

It was pandemonium. Very slowly, the buses had started to move away. Some mothers were holding hands of children through the open windows. Most mothers were crying. Dolly Blood, never one for hugs and kisses, was clearly upset beyond her understanding.

"Little sods!" she was often heard to cry when whacking Maurice and Dicky with the wooden mixing spoon she kept handy for that purpose. "One of these days I'm going to run away and leave you all. Then maybe I'll get some peace of mind." She would be like 'all hell let loose' when she got her dander up. Basically though, Dolly Blood was honest and God fearing, testimony to her years, when younger, in the Salvation Army. Now she was gripping herself firmly, no tears, and no weakness. It had to be done.

Dicky looked back at her gaunt figure, her face smiling, her eyes anguished. When the bus turned out of sight, she just stood there, her throat ached, her soul cried out. Some of the mothers were sobbing, some consoling. All would be changed by the experience.

The buses carried the mixed cargo to Cotteridge railway station where a train, especially for them, was waiting.

"Anyone know where we are going?" shouted one kid. One of the teachers said she thought it might be Wales.

"Not America or Canada?" someone else shouted.

"There's lots of U-boats in the Atlantic," said the teacher. "Some ships have been sunk, so no more evacuees are going overseas, I'm afraid."[2]

A lot of the kids moaned. Many were convinced they would be going to America or Canada and were disappointed. Others, however, were glad that they would be staying in Britain, as 99% had

[2] **Sinking of the Benares**
The government had set up a Children Overseas Reception Board (CORB), which arranged for children to be sent to USA, Canada and Australia. Within a few months over 210,000 children were registered with the scheme. However, after the CITY OF BENARES was torpedoed and sunk by a German U-boat, on the 17th September 1940, killing 73 children, the overseas evacuation was stopped
For survivors stories see www.spartacus.schoolnet.co.uk/2WWbenares

probably not been anywhere at all, few council estate kids ever went away for a summer holiday, apart from those whose parents could afford a cub or scout uniform and therefore able to join that association.

The train made its way through the suburbs of Birmingham, rows of houses, factories, small businesses interspersed with parks. Everywhere you looked there was the evidence of recent heavy bombing, large areas of complete destruction and bomb craters.

The snow was still about and covered a lot of the damage, making it all look clean and not too bad. Through fields and large pools of melted snow, past farm animals, some being seen for the first time by most kids and eventually pulling in and stopping at Burton-on-Trent station where the children, some fretful, some expectant, the rest somewhat resigned to whatever fate was in store for them, were disgorged, complete with their pathetic parcels of belongings and transferred by bus to village halls in the surrounding villages, where local people would inspect them disapprovingly before marching off with them. Some kids would be lucky. Some would not.

It was 8.00 p.m. Bryn and Michael Jones, Dicky and Duggie, were now the only ones left in the hall. A man was looking at the list and shaking his head.

"I tell you they are not on the list. They should be somewhere else."

A lady said "well it's a bit late now Mr Fearn, we'll just have to find them somewhere for one night."

"Where? All those who said they'd take someone have done so. Who's going to take four kids at this time of day?"

First Night

Bryn and Dicky were playing marbles, the two younger boys watching. Dicky wasn't too bothered. They'd had something to eat and a hot drink and the local folk were kind, if a bit strange and talked funny. He couldn't understand what they were saying half the time, lots of munna, wunna, canna, shanna, dunna. It was like half English and half something else.

They'd found the lavatories pretty quick. Michael had been holding himself for some time and was clearly happy about that. Duggie had got the attention of a lady who obviously thought he was starving to death because he'd got a bag full of broken biscuits and seemed reluctant to share them. All in all, things didn't look too bad to Dicky.

"C'mon you lads, get in the car, you are going to Roobottoms farm tonight and in the morning take your things to school because you'll be going to a permanent home tomorrow. Fine!"

That was Mr Fearn's way. Think, sort and do it. No hesitation. He owned Fearn's Garage in the village of Yoxall, had one of the few cars in the village and was obviously a man of action, but at the same time, too old for war service.

Roobottoms' farm was set back off the country lane about half a mile from Yoxall. Mr Fearn obviously knew where it was. No stranger would have found it in the dark. The car stopped, they all got out and found themselves standing in mud, muck and straw. The only light came from an oil lamp on the kitchen table dimly filtering through the window next to the door on which Mr Fearn banged. His knocking was greeted by savage barking and the imperative shout of 'Down Scab! It'll only be Mr Fearn with the evacuees'.

The latch lifted and the door opened to reveal a small, slim lady bathed in the glow from the lamp-light behind her. She stepped back, "Hello Mr Fearn, come on in now out of the cold. My word! Have you brought half the school?"

"Wipe your feet lads," said Mr Fearn, leading the way and demonstrating on the coconut matting just inside the farmhouse. The children trooped in, dutifully wiping their feet in turn, and then stood there, somewhat self-consciously gripping their bags, as they gazed around at the new and very different surroundings that would be their home for the night. Mrs Roobottom, for that's who the lady was, had a kindly look about her.

"Don't mind the dog. He's barely a year old. He'll sniff you, but he won't bite. He's probably looking for a friend, because he doesn't belong to us. He lives at one of the cottages further up, but he's in the way at the moment. They've just had a baby, so I offered to look after him for a few days, although I didn't expect him to be such a handful."

The collie rapidly moved and smelt each newcomer in turn and seemed particularly interested in Duggie's pocket and was trying to get its nose inside. Duggie, not used to country dogs, especially one so vigorously trying to wear his coat, was now trying to turn away without much success. Mrs Roobottom, realising Duggie was now a bit frightened, again shouted at the dog at the same time banging the kitchen table with the flat of her hand. Scab slunk away and lay under a large wooden chair, the like of which the kids had never seen before.

"Now that's what I call a real farmers chair," observed Mr Fearn. It had a high rounded spindle back, wooden arms, rounded splayed legs with cross spindle supports, and a thick lumpy loose cushion on top of the 2" thick seat.

"I sure wouldn't like to carry that far," added Mr Fearn, as he left, his duty done for the day.

Mrs Roobottom and her daughter Betty had made a few sandwiches, which the kids had quickly consumed along with the mugs of cocoa made with milk from the farm cows. Dicky thought Rosie would have been a good name for the very healthy looking girl of about 15 or 16 years. Her cheeks seemed to be permanently rosy red or she was blushing all the time.

Dicky was trying to get young Norman Roobottom, a very shy lad about his own age, interested in a game of marbles. Bryn was reading from a comic to Michael, and Duggie was furtively trying to manoeuvre a bit of biscuit out of the bag in his pocket, well aware of the intense and eager interest of Scab. The dog's eyes and alert ears focused entirely on Duggie's pocket.

"C'mon then, you must all get off to bed" said Mrs Roobottom, "You've got an early start in the morning. Just follow me and bring your bags with you."

Mrs Roobottom led them up the stairs carrying two candleholders each with a candle lighting the way. The boys, climbing the winding narrow stairs behind her, could hardly see where they were putting their feet in the flickering shadows caused by the poor light cast by the candle.

"Isn't there a light switch" yelped Michael after missing his footing once again?

"No lad, no electric here. But you'll soon get used to it. There's not many with electric light in the countryside. You must be posh then!"

"Their Mom's posh!" Dicky blurted out, "They've got a carpet in their front room."

"If that's supposed to be posh I'd rather live in your house," replied Bryn. "You can play and climb in and out of the windows, and all over the table and chairs, and make a den under the table. My mother won't let us do that and she thinks 'you're the limit,' whatever that means."

"I don't like it like this" Duggie said tearfully. He was feeling his way up behind the others, one half of his concentration on negotiating the bends on the narrow stairs, the other half and one hand clutching his pocket containing the biscuits. In the dark behind him, he imagined Scab to be getting closer and was mightily relieved when their bedroom for the night, was finally reached.

The large bed dominated the room, above which hung a framed picture of The Lords' Prayer. Under the foot of the bed was a large white chamber pot, the use of which would be a first for all of them, accompanied by much merriment. There was also a small 'pegged' rug and one bedside table.

"Well there you are then. You'll all have to sleep together. Blow the candle out after you've got in bed. Goodnight."

Mrs Roobottom put one candleholder on a small bedside table and went out, closing the door behind her.

It was very cold, no heating of any sort and the generous heat from the large kitchen range certainly didn't penetrate this part of the farmhouse. Bryn and Michael decided to put their pyjamas on over their vest and pants. Dicky and Duggie, both of whom didn't possess vests and pants, took off their boots and put on their pyjamas over their everyday clothes. The bed was so cold, it felt damp, and the younger ones became fretful. Dicky, by now used to entertaining his younger brothers, made silhouettes on the ceiling, some scary, with the aid of the candlelight and hand movements. By slowly moving his hands nearer the flame, he could make the scary shadows appear to be coming closer and Michael and Duggie would try and get their heads below the bed covers, the two older boys preventing them. The giggling and tussling soon warmed them up and they duly fell asleep, not before Dicky blew out the candle.

New Home

Next day, Mr Fearn collected them from school where all the new 'scholars' and accompanying teachers had been gradually assimilated into the school building designed for 90 pupils and 3 teachers. Goodwill, voluntary help and unlimited supplies of hot Horlicks helped the process along. The frustrations and near panic of the overwhelmed adults, being matched by the incessant enthusiasm and badgering of the new arrivals, now fresh and loaded with questions after a nights sleep. For the teachers, it must have been a nightmare! For the kids, it was an adventure. Unsettling? Yes! Heartbreaking? For a few, perhaps! Would they live to regret it? Some maybe. Would any of them ever forget it? No way!

Mr Fearn delivered them, except Duggie, to Mr Philip Armson's cottage in Yoxall.

"Your brother is going to stay with the nice lady who gave him the biscuits. There's not enough room for all four of you with Mr Armson. You'll soon be seeing him, no doubt at school tomorrow."

The car drove away. Duggie didn't seem too bothered. It was only the second time in his life he'd sat in a car and he was sitting in the front seat next to the driver. Dicky though, was a bit apprehensive and just hoped his mom didn't find out that he'd been separated from Duggie, even if for only one day. He could already feel the wooden spoon whacking his backside and legs. Perish the thought!

Mr Phillip Armson, a pharmacist, wasn't at home. He was off with his two dogs along the river Trent, according to Mrs Taverner his housekeeper, Mr Armson not being married.

"Mr Philip's taken his gun and he rarely comes back empty handed," said Mrs Taverner. "I wunna bother going looking for him. You might get something you dinna want."

She looked at them sternly from behind her thick rimmed spectacles then chuckled. "Well you dinna look too bad for townies," she said. "Might've combed your hair though" looking at Dicky, whose curly mop was always beyond his control.

Dicky felt uncomfortable under this scrutiny and wondered how he was going to hide the holes in the heels of his socks. You could only pull the foot part of the sock forward and fold underneath so many times before you ran out of sock.

One thing Dolly Blood couldn't abide, darning socks. Dicky used to try to alleviate that situation by that strategy. Pull forward – fold under – wear. Easy, until the original hole got so big it was too easy to put your whole foot through the hole in the dark. Then you would show them mom, who, while quietly appreciating Dicky's strategy and ever resourcefulness, would stuff the socks with a mixture of torn up newspaper and coal dust, wet them, let them stand for a few days in a covered box outside and eventually use them, mixed with a few bits of coke as fuel for the fire. Wartime shortages were not a big problem for Mrs Blood. Years of bringing up a growing family of boys on very little money and sometimes none at all, superbly conditioned and qualified her for what lay ahead.

Mrs Taverner, having been forewarned, had made stew, very acceptable to three hungry boys. She then took them up to their bedroom, an attic, only much larger than the bedroom at Robottoms' farm. Although it was at the top of the house, the floor was bare concrete and at one side, under the sloping roof, was a massive rectangular steel water tank, which Dicky later found out, had to be filled daily, from the well in the garden, by a hand operated pump in the kitchen. There was one large bed, a small table and a cupboard with shelves.

"There you are then. The beds comfy, I've slept in it mesen. The tank makes a noise now and again, but dinna worry."

They trooped back downstairs where Mr Armson met them, wished them a good afternoon and asked a few questions about their parents and what colleges they'd attended and what their fathers positions in society were. He gave an odd look when Dicky said he didn't know what his father did before the war as he was rarely to be seen, but seemed impressed when Dicky said "My Dad's in the RAF," and left it at that. Dicky wanted to ask Mr Armson about the whereabouts of Duggie, but Mr Armson gave a sort of dismissive shrug and left the room. Mrs Taverner helped them sort out their letters home before all going to bed.

Dicky's mind before he eventually fell asleep was full of questions, the most important being Duggie's whereabouts. He consoled himself with the thought that he had to be somewhere in the village and would see him, no doubt grinning all over his little white face, at school the following day. 'Lucky little sod 'as probably ended up in a cushy home with a nice lady who would want to 'mother 'im'. Yeah!'

That's whats happened and Dicky would see him at school next day. Smiling to himself Dicky fell asleep.

Main Street, Yoxall – Pre 1939

King Street, Yoxall showing village school – Pre 1939

New School

St. Peters School, Yoxall, Burton-on-Trent, was a typical small village school, taking pupils 5 - 14 years, the then school leaving age, unless qualified to go on to further education. There were two separate entrances to the building. One very large room, which would be divided by a large curtain for a variety of sessions, and a normal size classroom for the infants. 80-90 local kids were there normally and up to about 100 evacuees over the war period.

There were kids everywhere. The evacuees seemed to outnumber the locals and were much noisier and cheekier. Some were already in little gangs, possibly because they felt more secure in this strange environment. Miss Price and Miss Olorenshaw were doing their best to complete forms, registers etc., while Miss Baker, the school headmistress was organising supplies of school material, seating and hot Horlicks twice daily in the cold weather.

The evacuees came from two Birmingham schools, School Road, Yardley Wood and Pitmaston Road, Hall Green. Two or three teachers from each school accompanied them. Some evacuees stayed for quite a lengthy period. Some couldn't get back to Birmingham quick enough!

"Poor little starving so and so's" said more than one voluntary helper from the village. "Most of them look and act as if they've never sat and ate a proper meal and their manners are awful."

It must have seemed very odd for both parties. Country life was slow and methodical and based on seasonal weather, it being a farming community. The children went to school, after a very long walk of up to 3 miles or more, did their schoolwork, walked back home, helped with farm work and then went to bed. Playtime for most country kids was secondary to school and helping out at home. Except for a very fortunate few, a cinema show was an irregular visit by a gentleman with a home movie set-up (a cinematograph), old flickering black and white movies including one 'funny'. 3d (a little over 1p) was the entrance fee and 'The Loch Ness Monster' would be seen by most kids several times over a 2-3 year period, there not being much of a choice.

Where's Duggie?

Dicky had looked, in vain, for Duggie on that first day at school and was getting really worried. Several days had now passed by and he could imagine his Mom galloping round into Ravenshill Road, where the nearest telephone box was, and yelling down the phone to him.

"How's Douglas! You didn't mention Douglas in your letter. He's alright, isn't he?"

Dicky didn't like the way he was feeling. Miss Price told him not to worry, she was sure some kids had gone elsewhere and that everything would be all right. Miss Price was the youngest and certainly the prettiest of the teachers. She had started to wear brighter clothes than normal when at school and would frequently conduct her lesson to her junior class, whilst sitting on top of a desk with her feet on the seat, facing the class. The older boys, much enamoured of her beauty, would almost fall out of their seats trying to look up her legs and the girls would chatter excitedly to each other in the playground, about her clothes, her hair, did she have a sweetheart etc., etc.

Mr Armson came into the kitchen where Dicky, Bryn and young Michael were eating their evening meal.

"Your Mother is on the telephone and would like to speak to you. Come on."

Dicky's heart sank. What would he say? Of course it was possible that the biscuit lady had already written to Mrs Blood about the whereabouts of Duggie. Dicky had consoled himself with that thought. Yes, she must have. She seemed to be very nice. His hopes were shattered immediately.

"Where's Douglas? You must know where Douglas is for Chrissake! Why didn't you let me know he wasn't with you? The poor little bugger could be anywhere. You promised to look after him. You wait till I get my hands on you."

Mrs Blood was shouting and in tears. She wasn't a lovey dovey, kissy cuddly mother, but she was fiercely protective of her brood and only too aware that little Duggie had only just got over a nasty accident with an unexpected car whilst playing the popular street game 'Cock a Rusty'. Until Duggie could walk properly again, Dicky used to 'piggyback' him all over the place, much to Duggie's delight and the mantle of responsibility 'piggybacked' also. Dicky didn't mind because to him it seemed perfectly natural. His elder brother Maurice had looked after him and taught him, the day after Dicky's 6th birthday, just as Maurice had been shown by his Dad at the age of six, how to clear out the dead ashes, build and light a fire, make a pot of tea and take two cups, each with one teaspoonful condensed milk and two spoonfuls of sugar, up to their parents each morning. Without realising it, Dicky knew that one day Duggie would assume responsibility for the care of Barry and baby Laurence. That was the way it was.

Mr Armson, who could hear Mrs Blood's anguish, took the phone and very calmly soothed and comforted her with the promise to find out next day about Duggie and suggested that she phone the following evening. Much to Dicky's relief, the following day Mr Armson came home from Barton-Under-Needwood, where he had a pharmacy, with the news that Duggie was indeed with the nice biscuit lady and her family at Dunstall, a small village just outside Barton and seemed to be happy. Mrs Blood, on hearing the news was mightily relieved and told Dicky in no uncertain terms that Mr Armson was a gentleman and that Dicky had better behave himself or 'so help me I'll give you a good licking you'll soon forget in a hurry.'

'There she goes again,' thought Dicky, grinning and now in the clear.

The Fight

"So you're the cock of your school in Brum, eh?"

Several of the older village boys had surrounded Dicky in the schoolyard. It was the lunch hour. The Birmingham kids were used to two hours at midday but apparently most country schools saw the sense of one hour, so that most of the kids could help with farm work.

Dicky looked at the group and inwardly groaned, "Not another scrap already." A few weeks previously, Dicky had had an argument with a kid who usually stood behind him at morning assembly at Yardley Wood School. On this particular occasion, this kid repeatedly kicked the tin containing Dicky's gas mask, resulting in Dicky being challenged to a scrap after school. Dicky never looked for a fight, but the prospect didn't bother him too much, especially as the kid was about his age and size.

Mr. Blood – a poisonous little bleeder, never far from trouble, according to Mrs Blood, had done a little boxing whilst in the navy during the First World War and later in the Army, which he had joined because he couldn't get a job in the early 20's.

When Dicky was about 7 years old, Billy Blood had brought home 2 pairs of boys boxing gloves on one of his infrequent visits. As Area Sales Manager of Kleneze at the time, he was usually away in various parts of the UK working, or so he reckoned. Mrs. Blood wasn't so sure, especially when he had a thousand excuses for having little money. 'Always got enough money for nice clothes though, haven't you?' Mrs Blood would often yell during one of their frequent fights, augmenting her words by throwing anything she could lay her hands on.

Billy Blood, some 3" shorter than Dolly Blood, would take the blows and fend off most of the artillery whilst making his way to the door, which he'd scramble through and pull shut behind him. That delaying tactic would hopefully, give him sufficient time to make it to and through the next door to outside the house. Front door or back door, he would emerge red faced, flustered and relatively undamaged. By the time he'd reached the safety of the street, he would have regained his composure and the cheeky grin, which so infuriated Dolly Blood.

"Hello Mrs Hole," he'd call to the nosiest neighbour in School Road, who would usually manage to be passing by. "Is your old man out yet?"

Mrs Hole would hurry by, a cross look on her face. Mr Blood knew nothing about Mr Hole, who may well have been a very honourable gentleman, despite being rarely seen. That wasn't the point though. Billy Blood had a cynical mind and a quick tongue and didn't like to be on the receiving end of scathing looks, no matter how much deserved.

"C'mon you two," Billy Blood waved the gloves in the faces of Maurice and Dicky. "I'm going to show you kids a couple of things that I know from experience will be useful to you."

Dicky, even at that age, knew about Joe Louis, the World Heavyweight Boxing Champion and his forthcoming title fight with Welshman Tommy Farr. He'd seen clips of the two boxers on Pathe News at the 'flicks' and like a lot of the kids would pretend to be either. Maurice was a bit reluctant. He'd recently had a scrap at school and came home with a bloodied nose.

"This won't happen again," Billy Blood assured his eldest son as he surveyed the damage. "The next scrap you're in, you'll be OK. Just do as I say."

He put the gloves on both kids, showed them the traditional boxing stance and the basic foot movements. "Forward left foot, quickly bring the right foot up behind like this."

He went through the moves in front of him, calling out 'one, two, one, two' at the same time shooting out his left fist, arm fully extended and quickly back.

"You see, nothing to it. Just do the basic movement and you'll be alright."

The two boys repeated this movement several times before Billy Blood was satisfied they'd got the hang of it.

"One more thing, if I find out that either of you two have picked a fight, I'll take the gloves off you and you'll get my belt as well, BUT," and he grabbed both their arms, "if you are in trouble and can't avoid a fight, just remember this," he paused, then suddenly stepped quickly forward, at the same time shooting out his left fist straight ahead. Bang, his fist struck the boxing gloves hanging on the washing line, where he'd hung them. He quickly followed up with a straight right almost knocking the gloves, now furiously gyrating, off the clothesline.

"That's all it is, remember that and you won't go far wrong."

Dicky looked at George Wilson. He was a big raw boned youth about three months older than Dicky and a good head taller. All the boys and some of the girls had formed a ring around Dicky and George. One of the older lads was chanting

"On my left, George Wilson of, what's the school again? Oh yes Pitmaston School, Brumagem. On my right, Dicky Blood of Yardley Wood School, Brumagem, both champions of their schools and here to decide who's best."

Dicky didn't fancy his chances. Sure he'd beaten the kid who'd kicked his gas mask, went on to beat the Gutteridge kid the same day, also Reggie Kettle. Three in one day out of probably no more than half a dozen scraps in the previous four or five years. He had been called the 'cock of the junior school' but he didn't think he deserved it, as there were several lads quite a bit bigger than him with whom he didn't fancy his chances at all. However, reputations are a funny thing and apt to trip you up.

George Wilson looked very confident and was banging his fists together whilst gazing at Dicky. The fight announcer said, "Now listen, when I clap my hands, come out fighting and hurry up, playtime's nearly over."

He clapped his hands, George rushed forward to be met with a jabbing straight left to his chest. George's momentum took his legs a little bit farther forward causing his upper body to overbalance backward and he sat down on the grass with a bump and a surprised look on his face. Dicky, meanwhile, didn't feel too happy. His left straight arm had been forced back into his own forward moving body, testament to the lessons taught to him by his Dad earlier. Forward, straight left punch. It usually worked a treat, but this time not well enough. Dicky realised that George Wilson was just too big and he, Dicky, was going to 'cop it.'

The wolfish grin had left George's face to be replaced with a mean look. He wasn't going to be beaten by this skinny, curly headed kid, no way! He quickly regained his feet and squared up to Dicky, this time a bit warier. He certainly did not want to be sat on his backside again. On the other hand, he did not want to waltz around. It wasn't his style, which was all, rush, biff and bash and had always worked for him.

Dicky could easily see the next rush coming, being lighter and much nimbler. He evaded the first rush but got caught by a glancing blow on his head, which made his ears sing. The ring of onlookers was too close and tight for a successful evasive policy so Dicky ducked underneath the bigger kids' swinging arms and got in a few good thumps before George's arms wrapped around him, threw him to the ground where they rolled around, Dicky desperately trying and beginning to fail, to evade George's much heavier punches, which, if divine intervention hadn't occurred, would surely have 'done for him.'

The very welcome interruption, as far as Dicky was concerned, came in the form of a whistling cane descending on any part of any body. It didn't matter which to Miss Baker. She was the Headmistress, she was in charge and God help anyone who did not agree. Whack! Whack! Whack! George, being the biggest target copped for most of it, but Dicky didn't go unscathed. The punches he'd received didn't seem so bad compared with the stinging pain of a whipping cane. They both scrambled to their feet, ran after all the kids and by the time Miss Baker breezed in, her cheeks flushed, her hair tousled and one stocking free of a suspender, flopping below her knee, were quietly seated, grinning at each other.

"C'mon out here, Wilson and Blood and get your hands out." She paused to catch her breath, whilst lining herself up for the chastisement that was to follow. – Then, "No (*whack,*) fighting (*whack,*) on (*whack,*) school (*whack,*) grounds. (*Whack.*) One whack for each word and one for luck.

They scuttled quickly back to their seats, their fingers stinging and their eyes trying to hide the tears that were trying to flow. The rest of the class were very quiet. Most had felt the venom of Miss Baker's cane and no doubt some deserved it. She dished out all school punishment and rarely missed the spot at the finger ends, where it stung the most. If you drew your hand away, even slightly, you copped an extra one for trying. Miss Baker was a disciplinarian first and a teacher second, probably very necessary. (*See Bamfords letter.*)

Dicky, George Wilson and his friend Stanley Brooks became good friends and although George and Stan returned to Birmingham not long after, they would meet up with Dicky again after the war and have a few laughs at their memories of the stupid activities they got up to whilst at Yoxall.

Evacuation and Country Kids

Dicky and his fellow evacuees soon realised that schoolwork was less demanding in the countryside. Maybe it was a general thing as towns and cities were linked with manufacturing and villages were regarded as the providers of agricultural workers. Certainly this concept would come back to haunt Dicky many years later when he had to take urgent remedial action in respect of his own children languishing in a village school. Maybe there were just too many kids.

It was true that as soon as accompanying teachers found out that electric lighting was a luxury, that public transport was very occasional, that fitting in with local ways wasn't easy, that the nearest cinema, or dance hall, or large shops, were 10 miles away, that running water was only in the local streams or rooftops when it rained, that flush toilets were a rarity, the teachers were off back to Birmingham, where of course, they would have fewer kids to teach than before and wonderful hair raising adventures in the countryside to amaze and impress their friends and family with.

Miss Olerenshaw was not one of those. Older? Most certainly. Fussy? Oh yes. Caring? Very definitely. A target for ribaldry and fun from the village lads and all the other 'townies,' who she treated with exactly the same equanimity as her own school class? Yes! Yes! Yes! She took it all in her stride, no yelling or histrionics, just a long look through her thick lenses spectacles, a cautionary word or two and later a few words of praise for effort. Most of the older kids delighted in making fun of her, but the kids who passed through her class remembered a little owlish looking lady who always tried to help them and always had a kind word.

Dicky and two other children from Yoxall School had to go to nearby Hoar Cross School to take a Grammar School entrance exam. Scholarship Exam, it was generally known as. Dicky wanted none of it. He certainly did not want to go to some posh Grammar School, where he would have to mix with the likes of the Palmer kid in School Road who daily ran the gauntlet of the local scruffs whilst walking to the bus stop, resplendent in his maroon blazer and grey trousers. Dicky had already been to several different schools due to the fact that Mr Blood had changed his job. He instinctively knew that going to a Grammar school would mean trouble with the posh kids and further trouble with his pals at home, who would regard him as a traitor. He quite liked Yoxall School and felt settled. He looked at the exam questions, wrote his answers etc., as best he could, went back to Yoxall with the other two and promptly forgot all about it. He wouldn't pass anyway, so why worry about it!

The fact that he did pass and didn't go to Grammar school would only concern him many years later. Meanwhile schoolwork at Yoxall would carry on, blissfully unaware of its new responsibility to the influx of pupils, who for several years had the benefit of a more disciplined and advanced education system in a city. It was no fault of the kids, village or townies, but it was a fact that at Yoxall, if one of the teachers was absent, it was always an evacuee who was asked to take the class for a 'set lesson,' usually craft work, raffia mat and bag making, plastercine modelling or simply reading a story. The village kids, mostly the offspring of farm workers and other agricultural callings, were subjected to a seemingly relaxed mix of religion, reading, writing and basic arithmetic mixed with nature studies involving long country walks, where the malingering boys would take the opportunity to tease and sometimes try and tickle the malingering, not so shy, girls.

Organised gardening, under expert instruction was a regular feature and voluntary farm work was encouraged. Further education, whilst no doubt being available, was a rarity through ignorance, lack of direction and opportunity. Many kids would grow up, marry and eventually demonstrate a natural desire for better choice and opportunity for their own offspring.

Abdul Abulbul Amir

After only a few weeks at Yoxall, Bryn Jones and his younger brother Michael returned to their parents. Dicky wasn't surprised as it was obvious they both missed the advantages of home comforts and parental spoiling, something Dicky had never had, so didn't miss.

Their father had come to visit them shortly after they came to Yoxall. He came in his car and took the boys, Dicky included, for a ride round the country lanes. He kept the kids entertained with his rendering of an old Music Hall song, 'Abdul Abulbul Ameer'. He got the kids banging on their leather seats with an 'Old Time Waltz' rhythm, one, two, three, one, two, three, while he sang:

Digital Tradition Mirror

Abdul El Bulbul, Emir!

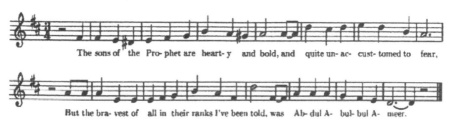

The sons of the Prophet are heart-y and bold, and quite un-ac-cust-tomed to fear,

But the bra-vest of all in their ranks I've been told, was Ab-dul A- bul-bul A- meer.

*The sons of the Prophet are brave men and bold and quite
unaccustomed to fear,*
but the bravest by far in the ranks of the Shah, was Abdul Abulbul Amir.

*If you wanted a man to encourage the van, or harass the foe from the rear,
storm fort or redoubt, you had only to shout, for Abdul Abulbul Amir.*

*Now the heroes were plenty and well known to fame, in the troops that
were led by the Czar,
And the bravest of these was a man by the name of Ivan Skavinsky Skavar.*

One day this bold Russian, he shouldered his gun and donned his most truculent sneer,
Downtown he did go, where he trod on the toe, of Abdul Abulbul Amir.

"Young man", quoted Abdul, "has life grown so dull, that you wish to end your career?
vile infidel know, you have trod on the toe, of Abdul Abulbul Amir.

So take your last look, at the sunshine and b

For by this I imply, you are going to die, Count Ivan Skavinsky Skavar".

Then this bold Mameluke drew his trusty skibouk, singing, "Allah! Allah! Al-lah!"
And with murderous intent, he ferociously went for Ivan Skavinsky Skavar.

They parried and thrust, they side-stepped and cussed, of blood they spilled a great part;
The philologist blokes, who seldom crack jokes, say that hash was first made on the spot.

They fought all that night,' neath the pale yellow moon; the din, it was heard from afar,
And huge multitudes came, so great was the fame, of Abdul and Ivan Skavar.

As Abdul's long knife was extracting the life, in fact he was shouting "huzzah!"
He felt himself struck, by that wily Calmuck, Count Ivan Skavinsky Skavar.

The Sultan drove by in his red-breasted fly, expecting the victor to cheer,
But he only drew nigh, to hear the last sigh of Abdul Abulbul Amir.

A splash in the Black Sea one dark moonless night, caused ripples to spread far and wide,
It was made by a sack, fitting close to the back, of Ivan Skavinsky Skavar.

A Muscovite maiden, her lone vigil keeps, 'neath the light of the cold
Northern Star,
And the name that she murmurs in vain as she weeps, is Ivan Skavinsky
Skavar.

By the second or third verse, encouraged by Bryn's Dad, the kids were 'joining in' and singing the protagonists names with enthusiasm and great energy. It was one of those unforgettable moments.

Dicky lost touch with Bryn Jones and his brother Michael, but years later learned that they both went onto Grammar Schools, further education and into management, as did some other evacuees who moved back. Without question, almost all children who stayed evacuated until they were 14 years old, which was normal school leaving age, or until the end of the war, were denied the advantage of further education, either at Grammar School or Technical College. Dicky, and others who had actually passed their Scholarship Exam, were still trying to get qualifications many years later.

Upstairs and Downstairs

Mr Armson, who was undoubtedly relieved that two of his charges had gone, now set about imposing some house rules. Dicky would at all times eat with Mrs Tavernor in the kitchen, never be allowed in other parts of the house except, of course, the stairway to his bedroom and to the bathroom and toilet.

Dicky would also have defined jobs:

1. Each morning pump water from the well up to the galvanised steel tank in his bedroom, which involved several trips to the attic to ascertain the level. He soon found it easier to check the level when getting up in the morning, estimate the required number of pump actions, usually a minimum of 200 pumps, to and from = 1 pump, check what Mrs Tavernor was doing that day, check any needs for the greenhouses and put in about 250-300 depending on time available, especially school days.

2. Help with the washing up of crocks etc., and preparing vegetables. Nothing new for him as there was always that work at home.

3. Scrub the scullery (kitchen) and pantry floor every Sunday morning on Mrs Tavernor's morning off, when she went to church. Mr Armson didn't go to church and never suggested that Dicky went, probably because he wanted Dicky to accompany him on his shooting forays along the river Trent.

Dicky, of course, loved these expeditions, he'd run alongside Jesse, the black Labrador and Ginna the little brown and white fox terrier, trying to catch everything and anything that moved. That was of course until Mr Armson wanted to shoot something, usually a game bird. Then Dicky and the dogs would be quiet whilst the world's most fearless hunter and greatest shot, would take careful aim, squeeze the trigger gently and − − −BANG! 'Oh Buggah!' Mr Armson would cry out at another miss.

Undaunted he would persevere, usually bagging something, even if it was only a slow moving pheasant or a dozy wood pigeon. Whatever, Dicky would have to carry the unfortunate birds back, sometimes soaking wet and heavy after being 'fetched' from the other side of the river Trent by Jesse. Mrs Tavernor would pluck, gut and cook them, sometimes in a pie, sometimes headless and belly up, baked in a tin with wild mushrooms, (the only sort in those days,) homegrown tomatoes, cucumber and various vegetables. All the extra meat provided by Phillip and his trusty gun, must have cost him a small fortune in cartridges, about four per hit, reckoned Dicky, but fantastic fun and he'd gladly carry anything to be part of it.

"Go and wash your hands and face and try to do something with your hair, put watter on it or summat."

Mrs Tavernor took the birds off Dicky and put them in the pantry and continued "Mrs Podmore is coming for tea, she's bringing her daughter also. You dinna wan' to look a scruff."

Dicky liked Mrs Podmore but wasn't sure about her daughter who seemed a bit 'stuck up.' Mrs Podmore always insisted that Dicky sat at the meal table with them instead of eating with Mrs Tavernor in the kitchen.

"He's never going to learn any table manners if you treat him like a servant."

Mr Armson would snort and reply "well he is a scruff, just look at him. I've had to buy him pants and vest because he doesn't wear them. He says he's never had any. We can't change him or his ways. He has to go back to his family sometime and he'll want to fit in, won't he?"

Mrs Podmore would have none of it, "come and sit by me Richard." She always called him Richard. Didn't like the name Dicky at all. She would explain the use of a serviette, which up to then had certainly puzzled Dicky. What he was supposed to do with this piece of rolled up cloth secured by a thick ring, supposedly silver, Dicky didn't know. She would patiently explain everything. Her daughter meanwhile, grandly smirking at Dicky struggling with the new concept of eating properly, "like the gentleman I will make you," stated Mrs Podmore, severely erect, her silvery grey hair piled high like the old Queen Mary.

45

Mrs Podmore bought Dicky his first decent book, 'The Last of the Mohicans', which mysteriously disappeared before he finished reading it. She didn't visit very often, so his manners and place in the kitchen didn't change much, but deep down he appreciated the fact that Mrs Podmore thought about him. He didn't know whether he liked her daughter or not.

Mr Armson had a sweet tooth and liked plenty of sugar in his tea. The meagre ration of the household was divided by Mrs Tavernor and put into 4 separate jars with labels on - Mr Armson, Mrs Tavernor and R. Blood. The fourth jar contained that which would be used for any baking, mostly stewed fruit, also to add to custard. Alternative sweeteners were not available yet. Dicky was well aware that he wasn't getting his fair share and that his jar always seemed to be quite quickly empty, as did Mrs Tavernor's, who also pretended not to notice. Mrs Tavernor pandered to Phillip Armson's wishes.

He was about 40 years of age, single and obviously quite well off. His mansion, that's what Dicky's Dad called it when he visited just the once, had once been a watermill and was called Mill House. It occupied about 1.1/2 acres of land, of which much was a narrow wooded strip and path between two small streams, which led to a larger wood containing plenty of wildlife. Dicky would go there and imagine all sorts of adventures in the absence of the weekly cinema visit back home in Birmingham.

Mrs Tavernor's daughter, Alice, a lovely, extremely attractive girl, quite old, probably about 23 or 24, thought Dicky, who idolised her, visited occasionally and sometimes stayed for a few days. Phillip Armson obviously thought the world of her too. When she was around he was attentive, cheery, and respectful to her Mother and even sometimes had a kind word for Dicky, to whom he rarely spoke. He, and probably Mrs Tavernor, very likely hoped that Alice would agree to marry Phillip, the only bachelor of four brothers. He was short, rotund, too much good food including, reasoned Dicky, his sugar and at about 40 years of age, far too old and staid for gorgeous Alice, who Dicky hoped, would wait for him to grow up.

Grow up? That was a question constantly on Dicky's mind. He certainly didn't think he was growing, seeing as how all the other kids his age were taller, except 'Wagger' Roberts of course, another 'tich.' Dicky seemed to spend an inordinate amount of time hanging on branches, gate cross beams, ropes, anything that he thought would help to stretch him, but to no avail.

"Gonna be a short arse, just like his old man." Billy Blood was 5' 3" with a 46" chest and short legs. Quite an odd shape really and Dicky was a bit concerned he might look like his Dad one day, hence all the exercise and hanging about.

Phillip Armson would let Dicky accompany him to his pharmacy in Barton-under-Needwood occasionally on a Saturday morning. They would travel the 3 miles in Mr Armson's little Austin 7 – ARF328. Apart from farm carts and the very occasional bus, the road would be quiet and Phillip would occasionally let Dicky take the wheel and steer whilst retaining control of the pedals, which Dicky wouldn't have been able to reach anyway. This was fun and would seem to be irresponsible in later years, but many farm kids had tractor driving experience long before the age of 14, also of general farmwork, milking and any work that required an able body.

Dicky enjoyed these all too rare moments of Phillip Armson's generosity and didn't mind filling and pushing the heavy wooden wheelbarrow with weeds and whatever Mr Phillip required. Sometimes it would be broken slabs for the many paths Phillip was constructing around and through his flower and vegetable beds. Sometimes it would be fuel for the water boiler to heat the greenhouses. It didn't matter to Dicky. It was strength gaining exercise and he was determined to get bigger somehow.

Change

The new surroundings, the seemingly vast countryside bereft of factories, large building complexes, traffic, people, smoke and noise. The many different species of trees, hedges and occasional tiny cottages here and there on the narrow, twisting lanes writhing through countless fields of various shape and size, most of which contained cattle or produce. The occasional lowing of cows. The distant chugging of a tractor. The steady buzzing of so many varieties of insects going about their daily business. The wildlife, rabbits, the occasionally sighted hare, badger and even deer. The owls, game birds and predatory hawks. The rural activities, farming, milling, saddle making and watching the magic wrought by the blacksmith.

Marvelling at the splendour and energy of the hounds and horses carrying their imperious, privileged, colourful, riders of the local hunt doing their bit towards the war effort. Visiting the local small town on market day, carried there by the little single decker bus which would wind it's tortuous way through hamlets and small villages, stopping anywhere at request and finally reaching it's destination. Sometimes there would be two buses on market day, usually though, only one and mostly carrying wives, all chattering and making the best of their day out, albeit a working one, helping with and selling their own bits of produce. Shopping and doing their own hunting for essentials not always available. Swapping family news, good and bad, with old friends not often seen. They might not be very well educated. They wouldn't recognise, or be comfortable with, luxury, even if it fell on them. They would grumble about the weather, the health of the animal stock and the price of everything. They would laugh at the farmer's jokes, help with any stock bought or sold, then travel back, still chattering, on the same little bus, grateful for the rest and change of scenery and ready for anything. The salt of the earth. It was all so different and the pace of things much slower. There were community events, church fetes, village cricket matches, whist drives, slow walks to church on Sundays with 'foster' parents, all dressed in 'Sunday best' clothes and the only day you might see a farmer not working for a few hours.

It was a big change from 'Brum,' the slang name for the city of Birmingham and its one thousand double decker buses daily transporting thousands of its million plus inhabitants to factories like Austin, Fisher and Ludlow, Joseph Lucas, BSA etc. and to big stores like Lewis's, Grays, Rackhams and the markets. The 'Rag' market, its hundred, or so, stalls under one roof, specifically for the poor, the thrifty and the bargain hunters. The Bullring, up from St Martin's church, an open market of stalls, mainly handcarts, anchored by wedged bricks or chained spokes on the steep, stone cobbled hill and where any small household necessity, food or otherwise, could be bought at bargain prices.

The little old man, always raincoat clad and flat capped, whatever the weather, patiently standing as if rooted, outside Woolworth's, repeatedly crying "andy carrier, only sixpence! andy carrier, only a tanner!" His left hand holding out a dozen or so brown paper shopping bags, firmly clutched by their string handles in his grubby fingers, his right hand hovering by his soiled right coat pocket containing the small change he would only get. The brown paper bags, plastic not yet invented, were indeed handy, quite cheap, but disastrous in the rain. Faggots and peas, jellied eel, cockles and mussels, hot baked potatoes blackened and salted, in a paper bag, for 'tuppence' (less than 1p). The swaggering travelling gypsy buskers, scruffy but cocky, "e'yar then! e's in the sack. Tie im up proper. No! Not you sailor! 'O 'orlright then. Now the chains. Pull 'em tight. No! not to tight!, you'll 'ave 'is bloody 'ead orf!" The humour was rough and always there, despite Hitler and his cronies.

The sword and chain swallower, stripped to the waist of his brown skinny body, walking around the watching crowd of shoppers and servicemen on leave, inviting the women and children to feel the large bulge of small link chain he'd just swallowed about 10metres of, the other end firmly gripped between his teeth. "For chrissake! Don't make me laff," he'd cry through his clenched teeth. Later, after publicly and horribly regurgitating the chain into a filthy sack, probably the same sack his accomplice would be going back into later on, he would pick up his bullwhip, flail it back and forth a few times producing the crowd drawing loud 'cracks' and yell, "e'yar now! I want a pretty lady for my next and probably my last dangerous trick! Come on now! Just one pretty lady to hold something for me! No!

Not you sailor! Haven't you got a ship to go to? Come on now, I only want you to hold my (long evil grinning pause) last fag in your mouth."

The grown ups would laugh, even though most of them had heard it all before. The kids, this was the age of innocence, would wonder why they were laughing. The whip man would furiously crack his whip again and laugh. He knew his audience better than they knew themselves and he knew that eventually a young wife, dared by one of her companions, would volunteer to assist 'The Best Whip man in the World' and be thrilled by the proximity of a half naked, admittedly a bit scruffy and mucky, obviously very fit male.

"E'yar then! My last fag! Just hold it gently in y'lips. And luv'ly lips they are too! No! Don't bite it! It's the only one I've got! Be gentle! Ok! Now 'oo sez I can't remove my last fag from this lovely lady's lips with just one crack of my whip! C'mon, any takers! Jesus Christ!, no wonder we ain't winning the war! C'mon now! I ain't gonna risk this pretty girl's nose for a lousy fag, am I?"

Crack! Crack! Crack! "Ok then. Here's the deal. Just one fag off twenty of you and I'll do it!"

Several hands would go skywards holding cigarettes, as the whip man knew they would.

"Don't worry darling! It won't matter if I make a mess of my fag now! Just pull that lovely chest in a bit! D'ya want a bit of help?"

So it would go on to it's successful finale and the collection of cigarettes and coppers proffered by the entertained crowd, including the still blushing and unharmed young lady, who would really have something to tell her mates now! The one shilling (5p) a day hire handcart transporting the only piano in the neighbourhood from council house to council house for the inevitable 'knees-up' at any good news, births, marriages etc. The colourful marching bands of homemade uniformed youngsters with their drums, kazoos, cymbals etc., led by a mace wielding high stepping young lady, organised and controlled by much older men, usually veterans of the first world war, at the many carnivals. Another desperately, but not despairingly, enjoyed feature.

The football crowds walking, biking, travelling by train and buses, descending in their thousands for home matches at City, Villa, West Bromwich and Walsall football grounds. The thousands of young kids and older men kicking anything that resembled a football through make-shift goals, usually a couple of jackets, regulation distance apart, on the dozens of parks and recreation grounds not taken over by the Ministry of Defence. The fifty or so cinemas, old 'bug-houses', many of them, were well used, very popular, with queues forming before each showing. No television for the masses then. The streets full of kids playing their games, 'cock o rusty,' 'leapfrog,' 'tipit,' 'marlies,' cigarette card flicking, rounders, one stump cricket (out, if you hit the ball into someone's garden or backyard).

These crowded streets would miraculously empty moments before the nearby factory hooter sounded, it being the signal for an outpouring of thousands of workers, most running to get a seat on the first buses away from the dozens of buses waiting, engines running, in the nearby streets. The rest, on bicycles, pedalling furiously, six abreast, to gain an advantage in their quest to get 'in front of the crowd' before merging with the temporarily congested bus and tram roads. Everything and everyone homeward bound. Within minutes the 'maelstrom' would have passed and the toddlers and older kids would emerge from the entry's, backyards and gardens to continue with the games they had temporarily abandoned.

The radio shows, ITMA 'can I do yer now sir?' with their wonderful characters held together by Tommy Handley. The big bands, Geraldo, Harry Roy, Ted Heath, Glen Miller, whose inimitable sound would conquer the world. The crooners and singers fronting the bands and the one and only Vera Lynn, the forces 'sweetheart.'

Just about everyone in 'Brum' listened to the radio, a welcome dessert to the daily diet of wartime misery and bad news. Many evacuees, including Dicky, would miss the radio as most small hamlets and isolated farms and cottages would have no electricity supply, therefore the war could seem remote much of the time.

It all seemed a million miles away to Dicky.

Malnutrition and the Kettle Kid

The angry red spots seemed to cover all of Dicky's body, especially between the fingers and the inside of his elbows. What's more, they itched unbearably and scratching just seemed to make it worse.

"Scabies!" declared Dr. Charles Armson, eldest brother of the Armson family. "Some of the children have got Impetigo, but this is everywhere on the body, except the face and head which is typical of Impetigo. Definitely Scabies!"

As Scabies was considered highly contagious, Dicky was kept at home and bathed and scrubbed in hot water every night, until all the spots bled. After drying Dicky, Mr Armson then applied an evil-looking green ointment that stung and smelt like horse liniment, before going to bed in clean pyjamas Phillip Armson had acquired. Clean but not new and they were too big.

This treatment continued for several days without any sign of improvement and it was decided that Dicky would go to an isolation hospital set up purposely for the treatment of Scabies and Impetigo. This hospital was a converted large country house in several acres of lawns, gardens and woods at Barrow-on-Trent, 30 or 40 miles away. It had formerly been Barrow Hall and presumably must have once belonged to a wealthy landowner. Now, although it was still referred to as Barrow Hall, it was a haven for about 30 or so kids, all suffering from Scabies or Impetigo and all spending approximately three months there.

For their first month, all new patients were confined to a ward containing about 12 beds, which were pushed outside on hot sunny days. They were only allowed out of their ward to use the ablutions, and the only people they were allowed to be in contact with, was their nurses. The second month they were allowed up and about, but to keep within their group, certainly not mixing with newcomers or those on their last month. This which was the best month, because you now had complete freedom to wander, explore, walk to the nearest village, and play with other kids from different wards, also on their last month. There were dens made by kids all over the estate woods. Bows and arrows were made and friendly raids carried out. All was bliss until the day the Kettle kid arrived.

It was lunchtime. The Matron in charge entered the dining room with a boy, holding a parcel. "This is Reginald Kettle," she announced. "He's going to stay here for a week or two. He hasn't got Scabies or anything else nasty like that, so you can all make friends with him and make him feel welcome."

Dicky, who, like most of the kids, was more interested in his food, pricked up his ears! "Reggie Kettle! Crikey! It is 'im!" The last kid Dicky had fought at Yardley Wood School. He'd beaten him too. He was much bigger now though. Not much taller, but certainly heavier.

"Now Reginald, all these children are evacuees like you. Do you know anyone here?"

Reggie looked around the dining room and spotted Dicky's mop of curly hair, "I know 'im, Blood." He grinned, sauntered over, as if he owned the place, and sat down by Dicky. "Warro, 'ow long you bin 'ere then?"

Dicky told him. Also about the things they got up to, the adventures and dens. Reggie grinned "great" he said and tapped his parcel meaningfully. Dicky sensed trouble and didn't have long to wait.

They'd all eaten and Dicky's little group including girls were playing around like kids do, in and out of the dens rolling and fooling about on the grass, some wonderment and mild flirtation mixed with a high degree of embarrassment portrayed. Innocent discovering stuff, giggles and flushed cheeks, just normal kids.

Suddenly, amid the frivolity, a girl's raised voice complained, "Leave me alone! I don't like you! Just leave me alone!"

Dicky looked across to where Reggie Kettle was sitting astride Doreen, who was lying on her back on the grass. Reggie had got a scouts knife in his hand and was tapping Doreen's face with it and saying "I want you to be my girlfriend and no one else's." He looked across at Dicky, grinned and repeated "my girlfriend."

Dicky said nothing. Doreen wasn't his girlfriend. They were friends yes, and maybe they might have eventually become sweethearts but they both knew they were going home in a couple of weeks anyway and unlikely to see each other again. That, however, wasn't the point. Dicky realised that Reggie wanted another go at him and obviously fancied his chances having grown a bit more than Dicky, who hadn't had a 'set to' since the Georgie Wilson scrap, an affair that taught Dicky a lesson. – Don't challenge other kids much bigger than yourself, but if you, remember what Dad taught you and aim for the nose. Forget hitting bigger, heavier bodies.

Reggie, however, was in no mood to hang about. Clearly very confident, he rose and approached Dicky, casually passing the knife from one hand to another. "Shall I cut off one ear then?"

Dicky backed away warily. Half his mind told him to get away out of it. This was stupid. Like most boys, he'd played with knives and dearly wanted a scout knife of his own, but not to fight with. That only happened at the 'Flicks' and the ones with knives were usually foreign underworld crooks.

"You have to use a knife to fight with now then?" Dicky blurted out, in desperation. He didn't want to run, but neither did he want to fight with someone with a knife. He couldn't think of anything else at that moment.

Reggie, still grinning snarled, "Nah! I can bloody beat you Bloody, knife or no knife!" He tossed the knife on one side and launched himself at Dicky, who, mightily relieved, met Reggie's nose with his left fist, following it with three more punches on or around the same target.

Reggie, his face dripping blood, came at Dicky again, snarling and grimacing, "I'm going to do you this time Bloody!"

Dicky couldn't believe how easy it was to evade the rush and bang home another couple of whacks, again on the face. Reggie stopped, pulled out a hanky to wipe the blood away, looked up to see Dicky standing there, fists up, waiting.

He grinned, "Okay, you haven't beat me, we'll finish this another time." He turned, picked up his knife and walked away whistling. Doreen and the others crowded round Dicky, who, although pleased with himself and the outcome, wondered when, not if, he would have to fight with Reggie again.

The next few days passed peacefully without incident until Reggie, who had been told he was going to another home, was leaving. As he got into the billeting lady's car he shouted "see you in Brum Bloody. I'll be ready next time." He grinned, raised his parcel and shouted, "I'll be waiting Bloody."

Back to Mr Armson's

Dicky, fully recovered and healthy, got back to Mill House to find nothing had changed. Mr Phillip Armson, who had been obliged to fill the water tank each day, was delighted. He inspected Dicky's body with approval and reminded him of his duties, which Dicky didn't mind at all. He was glad to be back with the two dogs he got on so well with. Jesse, the black Labrador, loved to go rabbiting with Dicky along the spinney, whilst Ginna would madly dash all over the place barking. On other occasions, Dicky would just sit and watch the games played by the two dogs and the obligatory cat, the latter necessary to help keep the mouse population down.

One game involved the old, nearby, upholstered dining chair, which was permanently in the backyard, at the side of the kitchen door and was used occasionally, for a few minutes rest, by Mrs Taverner. Dicky would move the chair to the centre of the yard directly in the sunlight. The cat would soon arrive, leap up and curl herself contentedly into a ball to sleep. Within what only seemed a few seconds, Ginna the terrier would poke its nose around the edge of the gateway, make a swift dash and leap for the chair, landing a split second after the cat's undignified leap for safety. The little terrier would then make a couple of turns on the seat before settling down with one eye on the cat, standing about six feet away, body arched. On cue, Jesse the big black Labrador would come bounding through the opening, launch herself at the quickly vacated chair and knock it flying and skidding across the yard. Dicky would delightedly replace the chair and try to entice the cat back, to no avail, another day perhaps. After a while Dicky would return the chair to its proper place for Mrs Taverner and look for something else to amuse himself with.

There was fishing, but he wasn't all that keen, he'd caught a few very young small trout on one occasion just using a net and being very still. He'd fed them to the cat, only to find minutes later, the cat regurgitating it all. Dicky would much rather be active like Tarzan, climbing, swinging off branches and, like Wilson of The Wizard, running against or with anyone or just by himself or with the dogs.

'Have you got something wrong with you?' Phillip Armson would enquire. 'Can't you keep still at all? Have you ever tried walking?' and other comments delivered in his inimitable, faintly aggrieved style. Dicky could never understand why he fussed so.

Beyond the stream which, when in full flow, used to drive the wooden mill wheel, once part of Mill House when it was a working mill for grinding corn, lay to the rear of the property belonging to Lester's Garage, which fronted onto Yoxall's High Street, the only road through the village.

Mr Lester, a small, bushy moustached mechanic-come-everything else, was the proprietor. He was also commander of the local LVD (Home Guard), a captain of the village cricket team and would eventually achieve fame as one of the oldest active cricketers anywhere. Mr Lester's wife and daughter, who together ran the little general store attached to the garage, paid Dicky 6d (2.1/2P) per week for tidying up around the rear of the premises. In the absence of any other pocket money, Dicky would augment this income with the deposit money from discarded (pop) mineral bottles he'd occasionally come across during his normal investigative ventures. Mrs Lester would also put aside a 4oz block of Cadbury's Fruit and Nut chocolate for Dicky when the opportunity arose, which wasn't very often as most popular confections were taken by those 'in the know,' the same old story with any product in times of scarcity. Dicky was well aware that Cadbury's Fruit and Nut was his Mother's favourite and he hoped to save four bars to take home as a Christmas present. He'd got two so far, tucked away behind the cups and saucers in one of the Welsh Dressers, well away from Phillip Armson and his penchant for anything sweet. With three months to go before Christmas, he felt sure he would have four bars to take home.

It was potato-picking time and some of the school kids had gone to one of the big potato producing farms in nearby Kings Bromley. They were collected and taken, all sitting on a farm trailer pulled by a tractor. They'd all come back at the end of the day tired, but happy in the knowledge that they would get the princely sum of £1.9s (£1.45P) at the end of the weeks work. Those that didn't go went to school as normal as did Dicky that first year at Yoxall. Scabies had denied him the chance to earn nearly £6 in four weeks!

Dr Charles Armson didn't think it was a good idea that Dicky should get so involved with dirty potatoes so soon after his illness. The popular thinking at the time was that scabies and impetigo were both illnesses associated with uncleanliness, only to be expected with 'scruffy townies.' In fact, both illnesses were primarily caused by malnutrition. So Mr Phillip continued to 'help himself' to Dicky's ration of sugar, butter and anything else he could get away with. Dicky meanwhile, would scrounge what extra's he could and would always be at hand in the kitchen when Mr Phillip's plate came through at the end of meals when Mr Phillip had bread and butter. Ever fussy about germs, Phillip Armson would pick up the pieces of bread and butter by one corner. He'd nibble the bread right down to that corner and leave it on his plate, certain in the knowledge he wouldn't catch any germs off his own fingers. He probably thought that as a pharmacist preparing medicines for sick people, he stood more chance than most of catching something.

Dicky, whose only concern was getting some grub in his belly, had no such reservations and snaffled these titbits and other savoury scraps as soon as they appeared in the kitchen where he ate the same food, more or less, as Mrs Taverner who pretended not to notice Dicky's scavenging.

Mrs Taverner seemed blissfully unaware that an active 11 year old needed plenty of reasonable quality food and Dicky had got used to being permanently hungry. The interminable diet of potatoes with one other vegetable and one egg or one piece of Spam was filling, due to the potatoes, always the same, boiled or mashed, leaving Dicky with a lifelong dislike of boiled or mashed potatoes. Breakfast would be porridge or cornflakes, with a spoonful of sugar, out of Dicky's jar of course. He would have one cup of tea with one very small spoonful of sugar in the morning and a cup of cocoa made with half milk and water and one spoonful of sugar at night. That was 21 spoonfuls of sugar weekly, quite a bit less than his ration. Dicky was well aware that Mr Phillip had bacon and egg and sometimes sausage and fried bread at weekend breakfast. Dicky would then sometimes get a piece of bacon, or an egg with tinned spaghetti in tomato sauce, which always seemed plentiful. He would also of course, wipe Mr Phillip's greasy plate with the corners of left bread and butter when it arrived in the kitchen.

"Don't you know there's a war on?"

Dicky, and other hungry evacuees would hear this lament whenever they, like Oliver Twist, asked for more. Meanwhile, Mr Phillip Armson and a few others no doubt, seemed to grow even more rotund; the plentiful food days of Dicky's stay at Barrow Hall now a distant memory. Dicky occasionally bought broken biscuits from the grocer's midway along the High Street. They were cheap, 1/2d a bag, but of course not always available and more than one little hungry kid would regularly poke his head around the shop door to enquire "any broken biscuits?"

Dicky's Post Office savings grew very slowly, but steadily. It was difficult to spend money really, as apart from the very rare visit by the travelling cinema and its black and while silent movies, cost 1p and sometimes free, the monthly 12oz sweet ration (about 6d) and the occasional bottle of pop, 2d, there was little else to buy. The kids, local and townies alike, walked everywhere. There were no swimming baths, cinema, cafes, school cricket or football, no school sport of any description, no youth clubs, apart from scouts which meant a uniform thereby ruling most kids out.

With Dicky's occasional birthday postal order for 2/- (10P) from his Mom, plus any coppers he could make fruit picking at Miss Baker's house, plus various other odd jobs he could find, together with the money received from his Mom at Christmas, Dicky would have a little over £1 saved by his 12th birthday. Not much towards his target of £10 to buy a bike when he left school at 14 years of age. Blasted scabies!

Dicky thought about his own bicycle at home in Birmingham. He'd paid 3/6d (17.1/2P) for it in the summer of 1940, money he'd saved from running weekly errands for Mrs Mansbridge, Mrs Arnold, Mrs Else, all regulars and occasional housewives. At that time, because Mr Blood was away in the RAF and Mrs Blood was working nights at the Austin works, money was more available and for the first time in many years the Bloods could afford to buy some much needed furniture and furnishings, cover the whole livingroom and kitchen floors with lino.

"Won't have to paint the 'bleedin' floorboards again" exclaimed Billy Blood. Very likely out of earshot and throwing distance of Dolly Blood, who hated that swearword. Whenever remonstrated to, Billy

Blood would reply, "Bleedin' aint swearin'. Everybody bleeds. Some people bleed on the inside. Some people bleed on the outside. And some poor bleeders bleed all the bleedin time!" He would be on the move well before the last line of his oft repeated stanza.

The Blood kids, Maurice, Dicky and little Duggie all got 4d a week pocket money, 2d each off Mom and Dad. Dolly Blood had been raised on thrift, lived and swore by it and would make sure her brood would know the value of 'a bit in the poke.' Duggie, crafty little tight-arse as he was, soon latched on to the fact that as the youngest and handsomest, well all the girls and Moms said so, he could expect to be treated most of the time, and his obligatory savings book soon held more than his older brothers books combined. He had to get a bike, a little 2 wheeler, secondhand of course, brought home by his Dad for his 7th birthday, mainly to cheer him up after his nasty accident with the car.

The same accident that 'buggered up' his possible career as an exponent of the art of 'tap dancing,' all the rage in the 20's. Little Duggie resplendent in his velvet shorts with velvet braces, brown, the cheapest colour available and white silk blouse, all made by Mrs Bentley. Yes, the same Mrs Bentley that made all the bobby dazzler uniforms for her husband's marching band 'The Billesley Arcadians', was a revelation in School Road, Yardley Wood.

He couldn't dance very well, he was only 6 years old, but he was 'having lessons,' unheard of in that neighbourhood. What's more, he looked good, black wavy hair, white cherubic face, smiling dark eyes. A few taps in his red tap shoes and a wiggle and all the moms wanted him. Dicky and Maurice could only look on and probably think 'little sod's got it made again. What's more, he's never had to get the fire going in the morning or make any tea,' which was true, but those times were changing fast.

Billy Blood had made a trolley from an old set of pram wheels, and some plank wood he'd scrounged. It could be pulled by a rope fixed to the front, or ridden down slopes crudely guided by the feet, which helped with emergency braking as well. An old fruit box was screwed onto the rear end of the plank behind the seating position for carrying anything, usually wood and anything burnable for the fire at home. Central heating was unheard of and only large buildings and homes for the very wealthy would have some form of radiator (water) heating in place. Whilst Duggie was recovering from his injuries, Dicky would be obliged to be his carer and tow him all over the place, much to Duggie's delight.

Maurice also had a bike, a 'Dawes' touring model with 3 speed Derailleur gears he'd bought himself, with the money earned working for the local Co-op chemist's shop on Saturdays. His job was to cycle to Stirchley, about 3 miles away, collect prescriptions and medicines for customers of the local chemist shop, carry them back in the basket of a typical tradesman's bicycle and up that 'bleeding' Parsons Hill, one of the steepest in Birmingham and which made most buses struggle. It wasn't unknown for the bus driver to ask the passengers and the conductor to dismount and walk up the steepest bit, much to the amusement of passers by. Sometimes a bus did not make it to the top and a replacement had to be laid on. Such was the reputation of 'bleedin' Parson's Hill, which Maurice had to push his laden delivery bike up every Saturday.

Dicky often wondered how he would get his own bike from Birmingham, but with no visits from his parents, not unusual as most parents were pretty busy one way or another, he'd long come to the conclusion he'd have to bring it back, if possible, when he returned from his Christmas visit home. Just a few months away now.

Potato Picking

"Sandy" Powell, an evacuee living with Mrs Elliott, a townie herself, who'd apparently evacuated herself to Yoxall and 'did haircuts' amongst other things to keep her 'body and soul' together, had suggested that he and Dicky should walk to Kings Bromley and try to get some 'potato picking' work. It was a Saturday and Dicky was wearing his 'quite new' dark blue, short trousered suit that Mr Armson had brought home one day. It didn't fit properly and Mrs Taverner had to make some necessary alterations including turning the sleeves up, but it improved Dicky's appearance, according to Phillip Armson. Also the pockets were big and the jacket had an inside pocket, the first one Dicky had ever had, which make him feel a bit 'grown up'. God knows what he looked like though.

They walked the 2 miles to Kings Bromley and seeing a tractor going up and down a field throwing up potatoes, they asked the lone lady picker if the farmer wanted any pickers.

"I dunna know, youm best ask the farmer, e'll be along in a minit."

"Oright! Just pick where she tells ya and dinna muck about" replied the farmer.

Both boys eagerly set to, running backward and forwards picking up the freshly dug potatoes lying on the top of the disturbed soil and putting them in one of the several big baskets at the end of each row of undug potatoes. Up and down, round and round the ever diminishing rows of spuds, for 2 or 3 hours with nothing to eat and drink, although the lady stopped and drank some cold tea from a pop bottle which she offered to both Dicky and Sandy. They declined, "dunna fancy cold tea then? Inna nowt else."

It started to rain, not very heavy but wet all the same. The farmer just kept going round on his tractor towing the flail, which would throw up the spuds two rows at a time. The lady kept on picking, so they did too. Dicky had half rolled up the, still too long, sleeves of his jacket, which were now covered in dirt and getting wet as well, as was Sandy's clothes. At last the farmer stopped digging and drove the tractor out of the field gate and away along the lane, but not before he'd stopped and said something to the lady potato picker.

"Perhaps he's gone to get our wages" Sandy said, as they approached the lady who was gathering her bag and empty bottle. She stood there soaked and muddy from the waist down, her head and shoulders covered by what appeared to be a rubber sheet with string through two holes which went round her neck and drawn in, so her head, upper body and top of her arms were protected from the rain. She held out her hand saying "ere you are, miserable sod 'as given this to ya both."

She passed over 2 sixpenny pieces. She turned away, then as an afterthought turned back and said "youm gunna cop it when youm get 'ome. The sight on ya, them's nice clothes too."

Dicky and Sandy looked at each other. They were speechless. Nothing much to say really. It was still raining. They'd got a 2 mile walk back to Yoxall and they'd got a tanner each. Dicky would never forget that moment and he supposed that Sandy wouldn't either. Mrs Taverner was a 'brick.' She saw to it that Dicky was washed and changed before Mr Phillip got home, laundered the suit and put it away without the master of the house knowing.

Dicky hadn't seen that caring side of her before and decided to give the next bar of Cadbury's fruit and nut he obtained, to her. He also thought he might tell her of his feelings for her daughter Alice, but decided not to. A gift of a bar of chocolate is one thing. A tentative proposal and request for Alice's hand in marriage in about 11 years time, didn't sound quite so acceptable.

Dicky would just have to carry on worshipping Alice from afar when she visited and spent too much time with fat old Phillip. He was probably a decent enough gentleman really, but Dicky didn't like him much, mainly because Alice presumably did. The fact that Dicky wasn't often invited in the dining room or other living rooms including the spacious sun room, where Mr Philip often entertained Alice and which he was never allowed in, didn't bother Dicky at all. He was used to his lifestyle and certainly didn't want to watch Mr Phillip fussing over his meals, commenting about this and that news in the newspaper he would often be reading. No, Dicky could do without that.

The time passed quickly enough. Soon Dicky would be going home for Christmas. All the arrangements were made. Dicky would catch the bus to Burton where Duggie would be waiting to board with his bag of clothes etc. They would travel on to Burton where they would change buses to Birmingham where their Mum would meet them, before catching the 13A Bus to Yardley Wood. Simple enough.

The departure day came. Mrs Taverner had packed an old suitcase with Dicky's suit and his few spare clothes, pyjamas, toothbrush, but no chocolate. "For Christmas day, youm gotta look nice for your mom now."

Dicky had gone to the cupboard the previous day to pack the 5 bars he reckoned he'd saved with his other things, only to find no chocolate. Disappointed and bitter that he was, he wasn't very surprised to learn that Mr 'bloody grand' Philip Armson wasn't too much of a gentleman to steal Dicky's Mum's fruit and nut chocolate.

"I'm sorry" Mr Armson volunteered. "Thought I would easily get some more to replace them."

"Greedy old bugger!" Dicky thought and wanted to shout '**don't you know there's a war on?'**

First Christmas

The bus trip back home wasn't without incident. Both Dicky and Duggie were prone to traffic sickness on buses and Dicky often had to get off the bus and walk the last ? mile or so home when Saturday shopping in Birmingham City Bull Ring with his Mom. Dicky and Duggie were OK on the way to Burton, where they changed buses, but with about half of the 30 miles or so to Brum gone, Duggie was showing signs of distress. Only 8 years old and still small, he was clearly suffering. A fellow lady traveller, who was obviously enamoured of Duggie's 'continental' looks, dark curly/wavy hair, dark eyes and a flashing smile, had got him standing on her lap with his head partly out of the open window while he fetched up the sandwiches and other stuff he'd eaten in Burton. The driver stopped the bus for a few minutes to allow Duggie and Dicky, who also wasn't feeling too good, to get off the bus and walk around.

"Got to stick to the timetable, sit at the front by the door, you'll be alright there."

They continued the remainder of the journey with the wind from the open door in their faces, both firmly gripping the steel protection handrail in front of them.

Mrs Blood was there waiting at the bus terminus in Birmingham. She'd changed and seemed a lot thinner, possibly because of the factory work she was doing. She also seemed tidier and she wore a different sort of clothes and a hat. Dicky had never seen her in a hat before, except in a photograph of his Mom in her Salvation Army uniform when she was in her early 20's.

"Christ! You haven't grown much, have you? Are they starving you or something?"

She grabbed hold of Duggie's hand and said "Come on, let's get something to eat."

No hug or kiss, like some mothers would greet their offspring. Not Dolly Blood. Fiercely protective yes! But touchy, feely, cuddles and kisses, no! More like watchee, catchee, tan your arsee! Maurice would describe her years later in fond memory. But Mrs blood hadn't forgotten their favourite treat when in the city centre.

They went straight down the Bull Ring to the cafe that served the hot steamed steak and kidney puddings, chips and peas. It was heaven. Dicky stuffed himself until he could eat no more and it was pretty obvious that Duggie, having emptied his stomach earlier, was intent on doing the same.

"Jesus Christ! You poor little sods! What do they feed you on in the country then? Grass?" observed Dolly Blood.

They both grinned and kicked their legs under the table. Dicky still couldn't touch the floor with his feet when sitting on a normal dining chair, unless he cheated by craftily easing one little buttock forward a bit, a manoeuvre which also niggled him because he knew he'd cheated.

"Can we see the gypsies with the rope and knives before we go home?" Dicky asked.

"Course you can, go on! Look after Duggie while you are walking around watching them. I'll be about twenty minutes getting some shopping."

"There she goes again," thought Dicky, "its look after Duggie! Just like before."

Duggie seemed to sense Dicky's mood and chirruped "you don't have to look after me. I'm 8 now and I've been going to school and playing on my own for a year. I don't want anyone to look after me."

He turned and fairly ran out of the cafe door, Dicky, now grinning, not far behind. Mrs Blood sat for a moment, gathered up the bags and small case, muttered "little so and so's!" to the other understanding mums drinking their well-deserved 'cuppa,' and went off to do the necessary shopping, wondering why Mothers didn't grow more arms when they gave birth. "Stick a broom up my backside and I'll sweep the floor while I'm serving up dinner" she would shout at Billy Blood, sitting on the arm of his wooden armchair pulled up alongside the table.

Billy Blood, very experienced and highly perceptive to Mrs Blood's moods and levels of sensitivity would usually do one of three things. Smile and say, "smells lovely and it'll taste lovely," go a bit red in the face and look seriously quiet, or get up and say, "e'yar then, sit down and I'll fetch the rest."

On the occasions he read the warning signal correctly he'd get up, move smartly to the door saying "just goin' to get something," where upon one of the utensils Dolly blood was carrying, would bounce off the door or wall not far from Billy Blood's head and the words "lying little sod" would career out of the open windows and petrify half the men in the area, guilty of anything or not.

The two boys wandered round the Bull Ring, unchanged as far as Dicky could see. It seemed as if they had never been away. The little old man shouting "andy carrier a tanner!" was still in the same place, as if rooted. The same faces behind the same handcarts, loaded with fruit and veg, household stuff, toys. The man demonstrating his magic solution "e'yar missus, rub it on a ha'penny and you've got a bob. Makes all your copper stuff turn to bleeding silver. Marvellous! an' only two and a tanner (12.1/2P) a bottle. Last for years. Mek yourself a bleeding fortune. E'yar then" and he'd repeatedly rub the stuff on his bits and pieces of copper, brass etc., on the cloth on the table before him. "E'yar missus!"

Of course the silver effect caused by rubbing on the solution containing copper sulphate would soon wear off and his retort to those fool enough to buy and even more foolish to come back and complain was always the same. "Well what did you expect for two and a tanner, the bleedin' Crown jools?" and everyone watching would cackle.

Mrs Blood found them easy enough, despite being laden down with shopping. She knew exactly where they'd be. In the open cobbled area, in front of St. Martin's church, where all the big acts performed. Sword swallowers, fire eaters, escapologists, knife throwers and their, sometimes human, targets. Whipmen and women. "Keep still now! Try and pull your nose in a bit, don't want to damage it. What are you shaking for? That's my last fag you're chewing! E'yar look, your missus wants to 'ave a go with the whip. Eh! Come back with my bleedin' fag."

The atmosphere, as always, was electric. There might be a war on, but the natural wit and warmth of performers and onlookers alike was not to be denied and only the criss-cross tape on the blacked out windows of the large stores around the market was evidence of a national crisis.

The 13A bus, after following its regular 30 min route through the suburbs of Brum south side, swung into the terminus outside Trittiford Park and discharged all its passengers, allowing the driver and conductor a few minutes for a smoke and refreshment from their personal containers, before commencing the return journey to the city centre. Dolly Blood and her returning 'brood' struggled up School Road hill, carrying the cases and bags of shopping the 500 yds to No. 221, just past the crest of the hill. It would be several more years before the terminus moved to a new situation about 200 yds past 221, much to the relief of those, now much older, residents at the top.

The house had changed, not on the outside, apart from the hawthorn hedge, which was a bit higher. The big and so obvious difference was to be found in the dining room, which now housed the Anderson air raid shelter, the top of which almost touched the ceiling and took up at least one third of the available floor space. Many families would re-site their shelters from the garden; the theory being a family was safer inside a shelter inside a house, in case of a direct or near bomb hit. The Blood family and all their neighbours were never unfortunate enough to test this theory, but many families within 2 miles of their area did, with considerable loss of life.

Dicky and Duggie were soon investigating all the changes and Dicky, now very adept after many hours climbing the various trees, walls, old wooden and broken down bridges along the spinney back of Mr Armson's place, was soon scrambling up and over the curved corrugated metal shelter to retrieve all manner of odds and ends thrown over by Barry and Laurence the two youngest.

Laurence, now 18 months old, had doubled in size and was walking. He was now too big to fit inside his own personal gas protection chamber styled to look like Mickey Mouse, the air supplied by a hand pump operated by a parent or other responsible person. The threat from air raids was now much less; indeed the boot was clearly on the other foot as RAF Bomber Command increased their night and day bombing of targets in Germany and occupied countries.

The following day, Dicky was up and out early. Most of his pals who lived near were out and about and making various requests to Dicky to say something. Anything! They just wanted to hear Dicky talk in that funny strange way which, of course, was now natural to him. "Y'shanna what? Y'munna do what!" The strange up and down slower delivery of speech and dunna, canna's amused them greatly, although within days, all would be normal again.

The few days before Christmas soon passed. Maurice, Dicky, Duggie and a few others had gone carol singing around the private houses in Hall Green, the next district to their own. These people were posh, some houses had a garage for their car or motorcycle and sidecar combination and most were generous. After the carols and the obligatory chorus ending with the words 'if you haven't got a penny a ha'penny will do, if you haven't got a ha'penny, God bless you,' they would bang the door with the knocker, or ring the bell. On a good night a few shillings worth of coppers would be collected along with various eatable treats consumed whilst walking between houses and singing the naughty words 'Good King Wenceslas, knocked a bobby senseless, outside Marks & Spencer' and one or two other proper ones when within sight or sound of grown ups. "Angelic little sods! Just look at 'em, all sweetness and ragged arses!"

Christmas was different this year. With both parents employed, Billy Blood had been released from the RAF because of his history of kidney problems and had now got an office job at BSA. Now there was money for a good Christmas dinner and some new presents as well as the orange, apple, nuts and sweets in their sock, which the kids yearly left hopefully at the foot of the bed. The war changed the fortunes for just about everyone. The obvious winners were the spivs, industrialists, chancers, those able to get employment for the first time and, of course, the survivors. The losers too were obvious, sometimes dreadfully so. Dicky's presents of clothes and two books, 'The War Lord of Mars' and 'Tarzan of the Apes', both by Edgar Rice Burroughs, were most welcome. He certainly needed the clothes and he loved reading. He'd gone through all the 'Just William' books from the local library just down School Road before the war started and he had got interested in the Greco/Roman wars, mainly because the uniforms and types of warfare that were so wonderfully depicted in the massive volumes, excited him so, much to the dismay of his Dad, who preferred the 'William' books. What did dismay Dicky though, was that the pencil marks on the wall glaringly confirmed Maurice's height gain of at least two inches, whilst Dicky's own mark had hardly altered. Christ! Wasn't he ever going to start growing?

Back to the Countryside

The trip back to Yoxall a few days after New Year was uneventful and Duggie managed it without being sick. The biscuit lady from Dunsmore was waiting at the bus stop at Barton-under-Needwood and they both seemed pleased to see each other. Dicky carried on to Yoxall not feeling very hopeful about his future with Mr Armson, who he had not forgiven for stealing his Mom's chocolate. Dolly Blood was not too happy about it too when Dicky related to her what had happened.

"You're not staying there she exploded, "The man's a greedy pig. No wonder you're half starved. Don't worry, I'll soon have you out of there."

Mrs Taverner seemed pleased to see Dicky when he came in through the back entrance to the kitchen, which was her domain.

"Sit yoursen down there. I'll make you a cup of cocoa and you can tell me about home. My word! You maun look after them nice clothes and look at yer, youm got some fettle on them bones."

She looked exactly the same, black hair streaked with grey tied back in a bun, same clothes and 'pinny.' The only visible change was seasonal with or without a big loose brown woollen cardigan and fingerless woollen mittens for any outside work.

Dicky grinned and gave her the little parcel containing one of the aluminium objects Mrs Blood had brought home from the factory. Like the others, it was a reject, quite small, all different shapes and used as toys by his younger brothers Barry and Laurence. Dicky had noticed one that looked a bit like an armoured car body, with a hole in the centre, presumably where the turret was going to be when machine finished. An ordinary candle fitted in the hole perfectly and Dicky had included one lying alongside a bar of Cadbury's Fruit & Nut Chocolate.

"Thought you might like this. It's a bit different to your old candle holder."

Mrs Taverner was genuinely pleased. She probably didn't get many presents. Dicky didn't know anything about a Mr Taverner and nobody mentioned the subject. Also he couldn't imagine Mr Phillip Armson buying her or anyone else anything, except perhaps Alice.

"Aye! It does look like one of them tank things I suppose and youm got me some chocolate, bless yer. I 'ope it enna bin too near that candle for long, we'm better eat it quick." She unwrapped and broke the chocolate in half, giving one half to Dicky, saying "We maun eat this up quick afore the Master gets back?"

They sat quietly at their usual places in the kitchen the only sound being from the ticking kitchen clock and the distant normal chorus of barking from the kennelled hunting hounds in the adjoining property belonging to Dr. Gerald Armson.

In the twelve months Dicky stayed with Mr Armson, he never spoke to Dr Gerald Armson or his wife, even though they only lived next door. He occassionally saw their accompanied daughter out riding Butons, her pony, but there wasn't any encouragement for them to speak to each other. Understandable really. She was a few years younger than Dicky. Not that he minded. He'd made friends with Buttons and would frequently scrounge bits of carrots and feed the pony through the fencing.

It was nice to be back. There was always peacefulness in Mrs Taverner's kitchen. Busy she could be with cleaning and cooking but once those chores were done she'd settle herself into the old cushioned chair with arms and contentedly knit or sew and sometimes darn the holes in socks belonging to Dicky and Phillip Armson. Dicky wondered where she slept as she was always up when he got up and when he went to bed. He would love to have investigated the whole house but the door to the first floor landing was always locked when he went upstairs to his attic bedroom and he wasn't allowed in the spacious sun lounge at the back of the property either. The only time he used the front entrance was the day he arrived with Mr Fearn a year earlier and when he went for a walk with Mrs Podmore and her stuck up daughter who Dicky would show off his climbing, swinging, running and jumping abilities to and who was measurably getting less hostile towards him. She was pretty, always nicely dressed, seemingly well educated and what Mrs Taverner called 'very proper'

"How far can you run Richard? How far?" she would say and burst into a fit of giggles. Dicky just couldn't make her out.

Mrs Podmore would say, "Now that's enough. Richard is doing very well. I can see the improvement if you can't."

'Stuck up' would giggle again, just for a moment, then look at Dicky with eyebrows raised, head slightly inclined towards him and purse her lips briefly. Dicky would be puzzled but aware of an increasing interest which would not have a chance to develop.

Mrs Taverner had a humorous side though and would chant silly rhymes etc., when Dicky was pumping water from the well up to the tank in the attic. Every stroke, backwards and forwards, would produce, apart from a small quantity of water, a raucous squeak and Mrs Taverner's antidote to the interminable squeaking was to recite a variety of rhymes she was familiar with. Over the years she had perfected a system whereby she would know how much water had been pumped by this method.

"One two, buckle my shoe, three four" and so on. Dicky, whose method was simply counting one for every two strokes, had no difficulty when Mrs Taverner was elsewhere, but when she, who could not abide the squeaking was there, she would chant, stamp up and down like a demented soldier, wiggle wet fingers in both of his ears and generally make a nuisance of herself until he collapsed giggling. He'd then have to rush upstairs to check the water level and finish the job undisturbed, Mrs Taverner having disappeared into the garden.

"Can I have a go at darning a sock?" Dicky had once asked.

"Course you can" Mrs Taverner replied and passed over a sock, wooden mushroom and darning needle. "Ere 'ave a go at Mr Armson's sock, but be careful to match the colour, 'e dunna like it if it shows up."

Mrs Taverner passed the large tin full of different coloured wool she'd unravelled from unwanted garments. "I'd let yer darn one of yourn, but the 'oles are so big yer maun fall through."

Mr Armson came through the back door, took off his coat and gentleman's country hat, stepped out of his overshoes, tapped the kettle with his walking stick, which caused Mrs Taverner to grimace, walked through the doorway to the living room pausing momentarily to look at Dicky and say "you're back then? Don't your parents want you either?"

For the first time in his life Dicky really disliked someone and looked away eyes smarting. The master of the house went on his way and Mrs Taverner said "Dinna mind 'im, 'e's probably got some bug from all them germs 'e 'as to 'andle" she chuckled, "poor bloomin' germs might catch summat from 'im." They both giggled.

A few days before Dicky's 12th birthday, Mrs Taverner packed his few things and told him that Mr Fearn was taking him to a new home not far away, so he could still go to the same school. Apparently, it had been decided, whether by Blood's intervention or not, to billet Dicky elsewhere, not that he minded, he'd had more than enough of Mr Armson and the feeling was probably mutual.

Second Home Yoxall

The olde Mill Farm.

Mr Fearn's car swung off the country lane and proceeded fairly gingerly down a stony rutted drive, over a bridge and into a cobbled yard surrounded by several old red brick buildings, a corrugated steel barn and what looked like a very old ramshackle brick and slate single storey cottage attached to a larger and much higher, better maintained, red brick building with a variety of doors at various levels. It all looked very interesting and higgledy piggledy. Dicky could hardly wait to investigate and the large sheep dog furiously barking in apparent contradiction to its wagging tail seemed interesting too.

A large man appeared from one of the buildings. He was obviously a farming type, wearing corduroy trousers, the bottoms of which were never going to be in contact with the tops of his sturdy heavy boots flecked with farm muck. Around his upper body he wore a three quarter length leather coat buttoned in two places and secured around his ample frame with a length of baling twine. Over one shoulder and slung around his neck was some more twine attached to a canvas bag in which, Dicky was later to find out, were a hammer, pliers, 2" nails, some binding twine and a role of 1/16" diameter wire. Mr Herbert Roe, tenant farmer of Mill Farm, Woodmill, Yoxall, never went far on his farm without his 'bits' bag.

"Allus summat needs mendin.' Canna move far without finding summat."

When he did find 'summat' he'd make a temporary repair and return later to carry out a more permanent job.

Mr Fearn got out of the car, as did Dicky. The dog, tail wagging, first approached and sniffed around Mr Fearn quite happily accepting the pats and rubs offered. Seeing this, Dicky confidently stepped forward only to be met with a growl as the dog, ears flat back, lowered its head and looked pretty damn mean.

"Nellie, that's her name. Just say hello or summat and offer yer 'and for 'er to sniff. She's friendly, except if you puts yer 'and near 'er feed bowl. Then she'll 'ave your 'and orf and 'alf your arm an' all. There inna much on yer" he chuckled and puffed on the pipe he'd been stuffing with tobacco and trying to light whilst talking.

Nellie, now sniffing and sensing from Bert Roe's voice that this strange boy was no enemy, wagged her tail furiously and happily accepted Dicky's pats and rubs, at the same time probably wondering why Dicky smelt of other dogs, Jesse and Ginna, whom Nellie would never have cause to meet.

The introductions over, Dicky followed Mr Roe to the end of the cobbled yard and turned left through a little wooden gate and up a path constructed of blue house bricks, past a water pump housed in a tall wooden casing, the 3" long steel handle protruding from the shoulder of the casing and hanging down one side, around from the spout from which pumped water, would flow at about 4" above bucket height. The path continued up through the garden, on one side a lawn, on the other, vegetables, to a tidy looking detached cottage.

Mrs Roe, forewarned and busy baking currant turnovers, greeted Dicky warmly. She was of medium build, greying hair, smiling features and wearing a full length overall, over what appeared to be, a few jumpers and cardigans.

"Allus cold!" Mr Roe would exclaim. "Middle o' summer An' she's got more on 'er than a sheep at shearing time. And takes a damn lot longer to get off" he would sometimes add, with a chuckle. "Come 'ere then, let's look at yer. Tell us all about yersen while youm eating a pasty, there."

She put a currant filled pastry turnover on a plate in front of Dicky and sprinkled some sugar on it. "Ere you're, get y'innards round that."

Dicky gratefully obliged grinning and wondering what else was in store. He already liked Mr & Mrs Roe, who seemed genuinely friendly and good-humoured. He'd liked it at Mr Armson's place, despite the oddness and coolness of Mr Armson and he'd never forget Mrs Taverner and her gorgeous daughter Alice, who he still thought he loved, along with Jesse, the black Labrador and Ginna the little brown and white terrier. He didn't like or dislike Mr Armson's cat. He just didn't understand a pet that didn't want to play and just wanted to sleep all day. Not much fun really.

That first evening at Mill farm was a revelation for Dicky. After the evening meal around the table in the living room, constantly warmed by the fire always present in the Victorian style fireplace and cooking range, no electricity or gas here. All baking, cooking and water heating was carried out on this very focal point in a typical farming house, Uncle Bert, for that was how they wished to be addressed by Dicky, swung his large wooden high backed armchair round to face the fire, which was about 6 feet away. His thick stockinged feet, now minus boots left at the door, he then placed apart on the home made rug covering the cold quarry tiled floor.

"Nice fire you'm got there Auntie" he chuckled. It was amusing to him, this Auntie and Uncle business, but he seemed to like it. He'd filled his pipe with the ready rubbed in my mucky 'ands.

"Can't beat it for smell and flavour," black twist tobacco he bought by the ounce in solid sticks in Yoxall. He leaned back, sucked and puffed, then leaned forward and spat a continuous brown fluid jet straight at the bars holding the fire. The spit hit the top bar and sizzling and ever diminishing because of the heat, made it's tortuous way down the hot bars.

"Dammit" he said "missed the bloomin' fire again" and chuckled, a tobacco stained dribble trying to find it's way through the stubble below his lower lip.

"Wipe yer mouth and behave yoursen.' What sort of an example are y' settin' the lad? You'm allus messing my grate. Look at it. You'm a pig. Inna no doubt about it."

Dicky loved it. Wow! If only he could spit, straight as an arrow and with power like that. He just knew he couldn't make that amount of spit, no how. Perhaps the smoking of that black evil looking stuff helped. He'd read cowboy stories in which the hero would chew 'baccy' and spit with volume and directional power and wondered if he could somehow get a crafty puff at Uncle Bert's pipe or cut off a small lump of tobacco to try chewing. Dicky unwittingly would mark it down in his immature memory bank, where there was plenty of room, only he didn't realise it then.

Apart from the fire, the only lighting was from an ornate oil lamp on the large kitchen table, the fuel for which would soon be Dicky's responsibility and fetched when necessary from Yoxall, or sometimes delivered.

"Dinna let it run short lad and you'll do" Uncle Bert said to him while showing him around, adding "and Auntie wunna be a mithering me."

Dicky's new 'Auntie and Uncle' listened to Dicky's answers to Auntie's questioning, Auntie with pursed lips, sometimes a frown or a laugh.

"There's nobbut posh 'bout us lad, no fancy talk or clothes, no tap watter, no electric or gas, no proper toilet, and certainly no car. No going shooting, onless we need summat for the pot. Only work and allus plenty o' that. The food inna plentiful, but it's good and ye'll not starve."

She obviously didn't know Dicky, he thought to himself, but he liked her. She wasn't funny like Uncle, but he could feel the uncertain reaching out of warmth from this God fearing, hardworking woman, who had been moulded by a life of drudge and penury as a poor tenant farmers wife, and been denied children of her own. When she spoke and when she was eating, her badly made dentures clicked and sometimes whistled.

"Gie us a tune on yer choppers then Auntie" Uncle would say, or "a touch of lamp oil on then teeth o' yourn might 'elp" much to everyone's amusement except Aunties of course.

Uncle, now sitting quietly, made no comment, just sucked, puffed and fired an occasional splat of well aimed expectorant at the now well splattered and stained fire bars of the grate, atop of which the suspended kettle would be heating up for the evening drink. Dicky would soon find out that life on a farm was regulated by animals and their needs plus seasonal affected product, crops, haymaking, harvest-time, muck spreading and in this particular farm's case, milling corn in the large brick building which was the mill after which the farm and hamlet of Woodmill had been named many years before.

In fact, the mill itself, could be traced back to the 17th century, ideally positioned as it was between a natural brook with a dam controlled waterfall and a man-made alternative sluice operated route which went around the farm and mill buildings to rejoin itself, thereby forming an island on which the mill, farmhouse, buildings and muckyard sat, fenced off, in the corner of a 3-4 acre field.

The farmland with the river forming a boundary on the one side, extended beyond the river in two directions to an estimated 10-15 acres and included one brick built bridge carrying the farm drive entrance from the road, one wooden footbridge over the lower river and about a 50 metre section of concrete stepped waterway link between the lower river and the high river. Directional control of the fairly constant water flow was by a sluice and dam arrangement at the high point of this section and damming would only occur several hours before any corn milling was needed.

All this, Dicky would soon find out about, but now it was time for bed and Uncle, having got through two more pipe loads of puffing, sucking and spit firing, "Good name that for a fighter plane eh? Dicky? Chuckle chuckle. "Tell 'em that at school eh! Tell 'em you'm got a spitfire at 'om, allus ready loaded and allus being on target eh? Chuckle!"

"Humph!" Auntie responded. "Anyone that knows yer and most do, know that you'm a spittin pig. Fighter plane? You? You'm couldn't get your daft body six inches off the ground y' daft 'aporth."

Bert & Tilly Roe

The Nightmare

Auntie made a mug of cocoa, half milk and half water, for each of them and after drinking it, showed Dicky, by candlelight, to his bed in a room dominated by a stuffed owl. The bird seemed to glare at Dicky from within it's glass container mounted on a shelf, high up, on a corner wall at the foot of the bed and opposite the window which, because of it's rural position, was of no interest to German bomber pilots seeking munitions factories in cities and towns. Therefore, the window was adorned with curtains, which were never drawn, except in summer to keep the light out.

The candle now blown out, the room was in darkness apart from the moonlight which filtered through the branches of a yew tree in the garden, probably, thought Dicky, the same yew tree that he and Uncle had urinated behind, before going to bed, the only toilet being a good twenty paces down an uneven path, turn right and another few paces towards the milk parlour. The path and the area around the small brick built toilet, housing a timber boxed-in seat with a hole, under which a removable free standing bucket waited, was tortuous and invaded by emerging tree roots, which were slippy in the rain. Company seeking snails, slugs and frogs added to the difficulty in negotiating it, making it adventurous in the dark, especially when carrying a swinging oil lamp that cast moving shadows.

"I inna gooin' down theer after dark" Auntie proclaimed "an' I dunna expect you to. If youm in need in the night, use the pot under the bed. But dinna forget. It's yourn to empty."

The searching moonlight caught and briefly held the fixed glass stare of the owl's eyes giving them the illusion of movement. The flickering shadows playing over the bird's body and wings imparted a degree of life, menacing and predatory.

Dicky now petrified and gripping the sheet to his chin, could only watch in horror as the owl launched itself through the glass and swooped down, landing on the bed at his feet. Wings outstretched, it's head, eyes glaring, jerking forward with each step, the fearsome creature made it's way up Dicky's covered form. When it got to his stomach, the wretched thing stopped, dug in its claws and proceeded to peck and tear at the bedclothes. Dicky, terrified, his limbs unresponsive to his mental urges to move, could feel the weight of the bird on his chest and was conscious of the sharp pain caused by its talons piercing his skin. As it's open beak slowly descended towards his face, Dicky made one last supreme effort and heaved the bird off the bed. He was conscious of the dull thud and sounds of the owl's talons scratching the bedroom wooden floor and the scuffling of its wings as it scuttled under the bed.

Dicky sat up in bed. He felt as if he was drenched with sweat, which was cold on his face and uncovered neck in the wintry temperature. He looked across the bedroom to where the owl was still glaring at him from inside the glass container.

"Bleedin 'ell" he muttered to himself, "I must 'ave bin dreamin'."

He thought about looking under the bed and using the chamber pot, which he felt he now needed, but he did neither and eventually fell asleep.

Next morning, Dicky stood on the old dining chair, provided by Auntie the previous day, and examined the glass container housing the stuffed owl. He was able to carefully lift off the glass dome, which he placed on his bed and inspected how the bird was mounted and secured to the wooden base. He prodded and felt the rather dowdy, very stiff body and wings, then just as carefully felt the hard glass eyes, now quite unthreatening in the dull early morning light. It was quite dead and looked ridiculously harmless. Dicky replaced the glass top, took one long last look at the owl and muttered quietly "bleedin thing!" Dicky would occasionally lapse into Brummagem slang. It was there, bred into his bones, forever, despite the mysterious Mrs Podmore's valiant efforts to make a gentleman of him.

Come and meet the Girls

Dicky quickly dressed, very aware of the new different morning sounds of a farm awakening. The gentle lowing of the cows in the milking shed, where they had spent the winter's night. The clanking of metal buckets and the water pump handle squeaking. The grunting of pigs, some near and others on adjacent farms. Doors opening and shutting. Dogs barking and all proceeded by the crowing of cockerels attending to the first of their duties.

He raced downstairs to find Auntie and Uncle drinking tea. Uncle, who Dicky had already sensed was going to be fun to be with, had quietly been cleaning, filling and getting his pipe alight. Now satisfied and surrounded by swirling blue smoke, he stood up, smiled and said, "come on and meet my girls".

Dicky was puzzled. There was no immediate evidence of other children ever being there and he wondered where they were kept. Dicky eagerly followed Uncle down the path from the little cottage to the farmyard, his searching eyes vainly glancing everywhere for signs of other human life. There didn't appear to be any and Dicky grew even more puzzled. Uncle's long legs, even at his normal casual pace, covered the ground at a speed that caused Dicky's diminutive 12 year old legs to overstride or trot a few steps now then and, his eyes being elsewhere, nearly bumped into Uncle's backside when he stopped at the entrance to a brick-built building, the door to which was wide open. He ushered Dicky inside without a word.

The instant Dicky saw them, he just knew that life would never be the same. They stood there quiet, but alert. Their magnificent heads raised, their large soft brown eyes glancing contentedly backwards at Jack Heathcote, the part-time help who lived in one of the cottages opposite the farm entrance. Jack was busily and gently washing their udders prior to milking them by hand.

"These are my girls, Dicky lad," said Uncle as he stood aside to let Dicky's eyes feast on the steamy peaceful scene of gentle give and take, the cows standing patiently waiting to be relieved of their produce. "There's only room for six an' I canna afford any more, so it dunna matter. The old one at that end, with 'er 'orns growin' round into 'er eyes, that's Betty. I 'as to cut the ends off twice a year an' next time you can 'elp me."

Dicky wondered how he was going to help, though he would find out quick enough.

"The next one is Mary, one of Betty's ten calves in as many years. Next to 'er is Bluebell; she can be ockerd (awkward) sometimes. Then Biddy, very quiet, she'll let you ride 'er, if youm a mind to."

Uncle rattled them off quickly; probably sensing that one of the beasts was about to evacuate her bowels. "Then there's nervous May, she's allus waiting for summat to 'appen. An' the big black an' white Fresian at the end is Ada. When you milk 'er, youm 'ave to be careful not to catch the pimple on 'er 'tit'. She dunna like it."

Dicky perceived the suggestion that he might be allowed to milk the cows, "Will I be milking them?"

"Aye lad. That's if you inna frit!" The unspoken challenge was not lost on Dicky. Bert Roe might not have any children, but he'd already 'sussed' the youngster. Bridling somewhat, Dicky immediately retorted, "I inna frit!"

Uncle Bert smiled and contentedly puffed on his pipe. "C'mon then. Let's go an' meet Sammy."

They turned to go just as Biddy started to raise her tail. Uncle quickly helped Dicky out of the doorway opposite Biddy's backside just seconds before the swiftly evacuated excrement hit the concrete floor and splattered outwards up to several feet away, including where Mr Roe and Dicky had been standing seconds before.

"Nowt much quicker than 'ot cow muck!" Mr Roe observed chuckling, whilst from the milk parlour came the sound of Jack's fury.

"Look at that! Youm a dirty bugger an' no mistek!' Why, in God's name, is it allus you? Now I've got to get another bucket of watter to wash your dirty tits an' another bucketful to wash the floor down. You wunna do it yersen, will ya?"

Sammy's excitement gradually drowned out the sound of Jack's grumbling and Biddy's plaintive mooing as we approached. Long massive pink body. Snotty snout covered with muck and straw. Glaring beady eyes. Noisily grunting and squealing. Sammy didn't have the same sort of appeal to Dicky as the cows had. It was obvious that Sammy would quite happily roll in her own mess as well as the straw provided daily.

"Why do you call the pig Sammy, it's a female pig?"

Sex education in schools wasn't an option yet, so any biological knowledge was learned by pure chance, much easier in mixed sex families, or from the playground, sometimes correct and many times not. However, Dicky knew the basic difference and although he was twelve years old, that was about all he knew. Like most boys below the age of fourteen years, sex was a subject for naughty, but harmless, jokes only. Leaving school and starting work provided the first curious impetus, mainly through what older boys had learnt from their elders. The main occupation of most boys below the age of sixteen years was sport, cinemas, youth clubs, telling 'dirty' jokes and trying to make their meagre pocket money last a week.

"I calls all my pigs Sammy, because I dunna want to get to know 'em. We shall be eating Sammy in a few months time, so I feels it's only right an' proper to regard every pig I gets, as much needed food for our table, not as a friend as I can say good morning to. So they will allus be just Sammy."

Uncle paused, sucked his pipe a couple of times and said, "Look at that, I've bin gassin' that much I've gorn an' let m'pipe go out."

Jack's Replacement

A couple of happy weeks of discovery went by as Dicky roamed at will around the farm and it's immediate adjoining area. He helped where he could and quickly learnt how to feed the new-born calf by putting his hand below the surface of a half-bucket of bastings (first milk) and letting the calf suck on his fingers. Auntie fixed him up with an old felt hat and somebody's old rain-mac that reached his ankles. Attired in these, buttons done up to the neck and covering the scarf wrapped round that same neck, Dicky was allowed in the mill to watch Uncle Bert grind the ton of corn that had been delivered by horse and cart a couple of days before.

Everything was fascinating and so different. Millhouse, where Mr Philip Armson lived, had once upon a time, been a mill. Now, according to Dicky's father, on his one and only visit, "it's a 'bleedin' mansion!"

This mill, with it's rumbling grinding stones, the rushing and splashing of racing waters pounding the paddles on the great turning wheel, the clanking of chain and banging of hinged trap-doors during the passage of another sack upwards, the whole cacophony of noises mingled with the ever pervading flour dust, was wonderful! Dicky was allowed to try his hand at anything and Uncle was the consummate teacher of anything practical.

"Anybody can learn owt, if'n theym a mind to. The younger y' start, the easier it is. I read somewheres that some Spitfire pilots were 17years old an' dinna 'ave a car driving licence, so at 12 like you'm, youm got a bright future me lad!"

It was still winter and if Dicky hurried he could get back to the farm before 4.30pm and watch as Uncle Bert and Jack Heathcote milked the cows between them, after cleaning the shed and washing them down first of course. During the winter the beasts would spend most of their time in the cowshed, which would get fairly mucky, especially overnight. With only pumped and carried water available, it was a laborious job and almost a losing battle against the over supply of excrement.

"Ow these big farms manage, I'll never understand! I've only got six cows an' some o'these farmers 'as got 'undred or more. Where do they put it all?" lamented Uncle.

"P'raps they inna as fussy as you" volunteered Jack.

"I bet a dozen like Biddy 'd soon mek 'em think!"

The rest of February and March soon passed by and Dicky was now fully integrated into the farming timetable, so necessary for livestock farmers, especially if milking twice daily was required. Being young, agile and possessing nimble fingers, Dicky had soon mastered the art of milking the cows, apart from Ada with the pimple on one of her teats. Both Uncle and Jack had experience of the swift backward kick Ada always seemed primed to produce, as she nervously teetered on her rear legs whilst being relieved of the weight of milk she carried. What a predicament for her! On the one hand, or should that be foot, she was grateful for the release of milk, and on the other hand, she was terrified of one of those big rough hands pulling off her pimple. *How would you like it!*

Dicky's main problem, whilst milking, was the cows' tails. Despite tucking his, cap covered, head well into the hollow between the cow's belly and back legs, the swishing, dried muck laden, tail would flail the exposed tender skin between the 'turned up' collar of his, old mac 'workcoat' and the peak of his 'turned round' cap, supposedly protecting his neck.

"Ne'er mind lad!" said Jack. "One day, in a few years time, y'skin will harden up like our'n. Then y'wunna even notice it."

Auntie had showed him how to mix the poultry food, "and dinna forget the 'Karswood'," she'd often yell from the kitchen, where she'd be busy doing something she now had more time for. *Karswood Poultry Spice for More, Bigger and Better Eggs!*

Dicky didn't know how it improved things for the hens. It tasted horrible! He also helped Auntie with feeding, collecting the eggs and the weekend cleaning of the two hen-houses, one in the orchard, the other in the farmyard. All the hens had the complete run of the farm and fields and mixed together, but they all knew which shed was their's at bedtime and were always safely in at dusk, the hatches safely shut soon after. Foxes were prevalent in the area and, cute as the young ones were, Dicky soon learned that they grew up to be wanton killers, rarely satisfied with just killing and taking one bird, but sometimes decimating all the occupants of a shed, carelessly left unsecured.

Dicky was also introduced to the workings of the mill which was operated by a simple arrangement of clutch and drive gear, allied to water power from a man-made reservoir, on the land above the level of the top of the big mill wheel. The reservoir was controlled upstream by a 'gate-dam', lowered and raised by turning a steel 'cranking' handle, the stream following it's natural course, round the lower confines of the farm and mill, when the 'gate' was raised. The day before milling was to take place, usually Saturdays and only in the winter, the gate would be closed, causing the reservoir, normally near empty, to fill. Then, when power to drive the mill-stones was required, the reservoir could be 'tapped' by pulling a steel lever on the lower floor of the mill, thereby opening a sluice gate which directed a controlled flowing force of water, directly onto the paddles of the big driving wheel, causing it to turn. Simple basic gearing would then drive the shaft connected to the 'grind-stones' and the upper drive shaft at the top of the mill. This top shaft, to which a long chain was attached, was used when sacks of unmilled grain were required to be lifted to the top of the mill, where they were opened and the contents tipped into the nearby hopper. Gravity and vibration provided the impetus for the grain down to where the grind-stones were turning in readiness to mill, the resultant flour descending once more to the ground level collecting box, where it would be immediately bagged. The sacks of freshly milled flour would then be lifted from the ground floor, to the middle floor, where the unmilled grain would be delivered and the milled grain collected. The lifting power was provided by a simple, spring loaded, 'clutch' arrangement, fixed above the top shaft and operated by pulling on the attached thin rope, the bottom end of which was at floor level.

It was a simple but ingenious arrangement, that did not require any great strength and certainly was not difficult to do. It took about

4 hours to mill and 'bag-up' a half-ton of grain and was normally done on a Saturday morning.

Dicky had been at Woodmill about six weeks when Uncle told him that Jack wasn't very well, would not be working there anymore and that he and Auntie would be very grateful if Dicky helped out. No problem! Although Auntie could be a bit stingy with food, never having had children, she probably didn't realise that growing kids needed plenty. She was however, well intentioned and always made sure he washed his hands before sitting down to a meal at the table with them, where she would berate Uncle for coming to the table "a'smellin' like Potts's cesspit!"

Mr Potts farm was at the top of the hill from Woodmill and the offending cesspit was the other side of the hedge from the road, along which everyone passed on their way to Yoxall. It obviously aroused much comment about up, down and following winds, much to Mr Potts's amusement, no doubt.

Dicky also liked Uncle very much. He was patient, a good teacher of skills, very funny and, best of all, a phenomenal spitter! However, and Dicky wouldn't realise this fact for years, the main reason he wanted to help was because he enjoyed being with them. They included him in everything. When they worked, he worked. When they played, he played, and when they went anywhere, Dicky went with them. Unlike his year billeted with Mr Philip Armson, he was now treated as if he was one of the family. A hard-working farming family, yes, but Dicky loved it.

John Hurst

The Reverend John Hurst, vicar of St Peters Church, Yoxall, turned up, as usual, for his weekly talk at the school. It was the first time Dicky had seen the vicar without his robes of office.

He was resplendent, a little self-consciously so, in a scoutmaster's uniform, the full works, complete with woggle, whistle, braid and what have you. His socks, held up with green flashed garters, were prevented from mixing it with his long, well pressed, khaki shorts, by a pair of the boniest, knobbly knees Dicky had ever seen. Murmurs of admiration, or something, moved around the classroom as, red-faced and pursed lips, Mr Hurst waited for the uninterested silence he usually received.

"Thank you boys and girls. Thank you. Come on now, I've got some good news for you all."

"E's leavin'." Pete Sharratt whispered, the trigger for a few giggles around him.

"'E wunna get far on them legs" giggled 'Wagger' Roberts and the ribaldry broke out again.

"Sharratt! Roberts! Blood! Mewis! And you!, you!, you!, you!." Each shout, each word, was accompanied by a whack from the cane Miss Baker was wielding and using like a miniature Bodacea as she bounced amongst them.

"Get out! Get out! Into my study. Now!"

Whack! Whack! Whack! The kids, some still giggling, the unlucky ones already smarting, wended their way hurriedly through the large classroom and filed into the headmistress's study where they waited for the shouting, threatening, volatile, 4ft 10" eruption called Miss Delphina Baker, to finish haranguing the rest of the children, probably terrifying the vicar as well. They didn't have long to wait. The door burst open. The pointing cane, after imperiously indicating a single line, both hands outstretched palms up, whistled down, Whack! Whack! Whack! Three for each hand. Chrissake! You didn't know where to put them, the fingers stung so. Writing, untying things or picking your nose was out of the question for at least half an hour. Miss Baker, her fury now abated, motioned them out and closed the door. She was probably cursing the day she decided to be the headmistress of a nice quiet village school.

Mr Hurst, having now got the uninterested silence he preferred, started again. "Does anyone know what this is?" He held aloft a small piece of wood about 9" long and about 1" diameter.

"Looks like a leg off a milking stool," called out one of the farm boys.

"Inna bin doin' a bit o' crafty milkin,' 'ave ya?" called out another.

"No, I haven't been doing a bit of crafty milking," replied Mr Hurst. "But I have been known to bounce something like this off a few choir boys heads" and he smiled. He was the vicar, solemn, serious and perhaps a little shy, but he'd shown an unexpected sense of humour and the listening kids warmed to him.

"Yes, this is a leg off a milking stool, or to be more correct, the leg off a small chair. I've cut it down to this size in order that it be comfortable to carry in one hand and pass on to another person's hand"

The kids, now thoroughly bemused and convinced that their vicar had at last 'gone off his rocker,' waited expectantly for the next piece of nonsensical verbosity which, at the very least, was mystifying and entertaining.

"Now who would want to pass on a piece of wood like this and who, by the same token, would want to receive it? Mmn? Mmn?"

The listening wide-eyed kids were perplexed, silent and instinctively aware that all was about to be revealed.

"Ah! Got you there, haven't I" chortled the oh so solemn and serious John Hurst, vicar of St Peters Church in the parish of Yoxall, Burton on Trent, Staffordshire. England.

"In the right circumstances, in this case a relay race, two runners would be involved in the passing and receiving of this baton, for that is what this chair leg is going to be. We are going to form two relay teams, one for boys and one for girls and four runners in each team. I am going to train the teams to correctly pass the baton in relay racing. The purpose of a relay race is to get the baton from the start line to the finish line first and at least two teams take part. I intend to get other schools interested so that we will have someone to race against."

He paused, flushed and happy in the sure knowledge that he had captured these deprived kids attention. He was fully aware that this village school, like many others, had no sports facilities and equipment, that most kids would leave school never having played cricket or football, the UK national sports. However, the school did have a field, called the Lea, in which the school was set and was big enough to mark out a 220yds running track on. What's more, the kids all had two legs and bags of energy. A homemade baton was a very inexpensive piece of sports equipment.

Mr Hurst now struck an energetic pose of a runner about to pass on the baton from his extended hand, his trailing arm and open hand stuck out behind him. He then turned through 180 degrees holding the same pose, but now with the baton in his trailing hand. He repeated this movement a couple of times, breasted an imaginary finishing line, resumed his normal position and beamed "who wants to be in my relay teams?"

A forest of arms shot up. It was one of those defining moments, maybe for John Hurst who had, for the first time, got the undivided attention of all the children there. Maybe for the children who, for the first time, were seeing their vicar in a wholly new light. But certainly for Dicky Blood, in whom, suddenly and unexpectedly, had been awakened an intense interest in competitive running, which would remain with him for the rest of his life.

Within a couple of weeks, John Hurst, with the enthusiastic help of several of the boys, had marked out with whitewash, a 220yds track on the Lea, the 'sports' field behind the school. Some divine inspiration, plus a borrowed mower, produced, what was probably, the first oval 'crop' circle. Except it was in grass. Whatever, St Peter's school now had a 'running track.'

Mr Hurst then asked all those in the top class to prepare themselves in order to run as fast as they can round one lap of the track. Prepare themselves? What did he mean, prepare themselves? John Hurst had anticipated the situation and was ready and in his scout uniform, "Observe and learn" he said.

He then trotted up and down for a couple of minutes, walked to the start line, crouched, loudly called out "ready, steady, Go!" and launched himself off round the track in a style which suggested considerable experience in track running. He maintained the fast even pace all the way round and finished breasting an imaginary tape in great triumph. He might be a shy vicar, but he was a show-off and a worthy one, too.

"Right! I'm going to call you forward, one at a time, start you and time you with this watch," he held up a large shiny, steel cased, watch.

The kids all crowded forward, "can't we all run together sir?" one called out.

"No!" answered the vicar, "I want to time you all as you run on your own and also see what you've got on your feet."

One by one, the kids ran one lap each as fast as they could. Dot Plant, as most of the boys already knew 'could shift a bit,' went round in 33 sec. As did several of the boys, including Dicky, Bob Mewis and Peter Sharratt. There were several slower times, but none faster than 33 sec.

"Well done! Dorothy, well done!" and a not so enthusiastic "well done boys" from Mr Hurst, who then advised them all to try and get some 'pumps' (plimsolls) to race in.

"You won't be able to run in hobnail boots when you're in my team" he said, and continued, "You'll need shorts and vests as well. The school can provide coloured team sashes and I will provide the baton and training.

During the last two summers of Dicky's stay at Yoxall, John Hurst trained and developed relay teams to compete, very successfully, against other school teams in the Burton-on-Trent area and Dicky, thanks to John Hurst's enthusiasm, had found something he was good at.

"Third player plays 'igh"

Saturday night, in Dicky's opinion, was the best night of the week. Constable Northwood, the one and only, much respected, village policeman, would arrive on his pushbike about 7pm. After a general chit-chat about this and that by the adults, they all would make their way into the warm lounge, where everything was prepared. Oil lamps lit. Fire, which had been going for several hours, freshly stoked up with dry logs. More available in the nearby scuttle, filled earlier by Dicky. The card table, complete with cards, already unfolded and erected.

Auntie would be carrying writing pad, pencil and a tin of biscuits. Uncle would be carrying the quart of beer Dicky had fetched earlier on his bike, from the outdoor sales of the pub at Hadley End. Minus, of course, the mouthful Dicky would have on the way back, courtesy of the understanding barman, who would always completely fill the quart bottle after previously showing Dicky the actual quart level at just below the neck.

Mr Northwood would be nursing his helmet containing his bicycle clips and gloves and Dicky would have 'pop' for Auntie and himself and be wearing a big grin in anticipation of the game ahead, which he was now capable of playing, after several weeks' participation. Nellie would skulk behind determined, somehow, to get by and lay unseen on one of the homemade 'pegged' rugs, which helped cover the cold, stone tiled, floor.

In the centre of the room, stood the well polished dining table which, in the two years Dicky stayed there, would never be used. This was the 'best room' and just about every farmhouse and cottage had one. They were rarely used, except for weddings, funerals, Christmas dinner, visiting doctor or vicar and, of course, the land owning gentry, or his representative, on his annual inspection, possibly with a mind to setting a rent increase.

Everything in the 'best room' was the best and reflected the stoic carefulness of the occupiers. Polished wooden framed, sepia coloured, photographs of solemn faced relatives, posing in 'Sunday best' clothes, adorned the walls, mantelpieces, sideboards, window sills etc. Apart from a grandfather clock, very often in the hallway, a wall clock, often a 'long service' employment award, would occupy a prominent wall position. A piano and, or, a 'wind up' gramophone or phonograph was essential, as was a 'wireless' on which just 2 stations were readily available, the BBC Home service and the BBC Light Programme, the only sources of communicated entertainment, including the cheeky broadcasts by 'Lord Haw-haw'. His real name was William Joyce, the American born traitor lauding the advantages for Britain giving in to the Germans, and later hung as a traitor.

There would also be at least three or four brass oil lamps, most being highly decorative but not all being used at the same time. There would not be bunches of flowers. The 'working class', town or rural, could not afford to pay for cut flowers. What's more, they would not see the sense in paying good, hard earned money, for something that was already dying, especially as they looked so much better and lasted longer in their natural surroundings, of which there was plenty in and around Yoxall.

The favourite card game was Whist and it wasn't long before Dicky was competent enough to accompany Auntie to the weekly village 'Whist drive' in the church hall, where he would partner Auntie with reasonable success, the half time tea and biscuits being a bonus for the ever-hungry boy.

Occasionally, it would be 'progressive' Whist, where instead of keeping your partner, you split up and had a different partner each game. Dicky, although shy in the company of adults, coped well enough, until one night, he moved and was obliged to partner 'Old Misery Guts,' an unsmiling lady of advancing years who looked and talked as if her mouth housed someone else's dentures, which moved independently of her own gums, even when she wasn't grumbling. The incessant clicking and dribble of escaping saliva 'making a run for it,' didn't help. Neither did her reaction to Dicky, as second player, following suit with an Ace, being the only card he had in that suit.

'Old Misery Guts' sucked in the saliva, clamped shut her lips to prevent her dentures flying out, stood up, leaned over the table and clouted Dicky with her free hand. "Y' young fool!. Dinna y' know nowt? Second player plays low, third player plays 'igh!" She paused to slurp and click a bit, then continued, "If y'canna play cards y' should be at yom!" (home).

Dicky, rubbing his tingling ear, said very aggrievedly "I only 'ad the Ace in that suit."

The other players added their protestations in support of Dicky, but 'Old Misery Guts wasn't put off

"It dunna matter what y'say, slurp! Click! Click! 'e should 'ave played it fust, slurp!, click!, suck!".

"'e never 'ad the lead to play it fust, y' miserable old bugger!" whispered one of the women at the table, loud enough for everyone to hear, including the vicar, Mr Hurst, organiser and keen supporter of all village events.

"Now, now! Ladies," he called out, affecting his 'church sermon style' voice. "Remember, we are all friends here and all on the same side. We can well do without arguing and blasphemy, especially on church property!"

The last few words were spoken as his bespectacled gaze remained steadfastly fixed on the lady who had sworn.

"Dammit! Now look what youm done," she angrily whispered to 'Old Misery Guts.' Click! Click! Slurp! Suck! And a defiant toss of the head was all she got back, which was lucky, as 'Old Misery Gut's mouth was open and she could easily have got her rebellious teeth as well.

The night's game continued and 'Old Misery Guts' won the second prize of six fresh eggs. The applause she received was muted, apart from Mr Hurst's vigorous, loud clapping in support of fairness, equanimity, forgiveness and everything else he passionately believed in. A good man, severely misunderstood by many of his young parishioners.

Education? What's That?

Potato picking had finished and everything was back to normal, except, of course, some of the kids were financially a lot better off and would have preferred to carry on working instead of having to waste their time going to school. That is how most of the children viewed it. School was more of a way of passing time than a centre of learning. As the number of evacueed children gradually reduced, mainly due to the enormous reduction in enemy bombing activity over Birmingham and subsequent lessening of danger, so the number of teaching staff reduced as accompanying teachers also went back home.

It must have been a chaotic time for the head mistress, Miss Delphina Baker, soon to be married to a Mr Ward. She probably never quite recovered from the influx and onslaught of all those horrible 'townies' and the enormous strain on the existing school resources. It certainly wasn't the children's fault that teaching was somewhat spasmodic. It seemed to Dicky, on reflection many years later, that much time was spent on 'raffia' bag-making, plasticine modelling, school gardening, scripture work, nature walks and for the older ones, usually evacuees, taking the infant class when Mrs Bates was poorly.

Apart from the relay racing that the vicar had organised, with competitions with other schools, Newborough, Marchington and Kings Bromley, to name a few, there were no football, cricket or netball teams. The simple reason being, that there was no sports equipment and never had been in the 3 years that Dicky was at Yoxall. But there was skipping. Yes! There were enough skipping ropes to satisfy the demands of girls AND boys. Anything was better than nowt!

Winter weather also must have caused many problems. There wasn't a bus service. There were no 'lifts' by car. There were probably no more than half a dozen cars in and around Yoxall anyway. What's more, petrol was rationed and unnecessary use was frowned on. If the weather was really bad with heavy rain or snow, the children were encouraged to stay at home. The parents were aware that most teachers would not attend and some parents would be glad of the 'extra' help at home anyway. Bearing in mind that most kids lived outside the village and that some had to walk up to 2 miles each way, even 5 year olds, the present generation of kids and parents must wonder how some of the wartime kids in the countryside got any education at all!

Christmas passed by uneventfully, apart from the usual week at home in Yardley Wood, where Dicky sensed that Maurice was growing up, in every way. Although only 22 months older than Dicky, Moss was now much taller, had a girlfriend, smoked 'Players' cigarettes and seemed to know everything about entertainment on the wireless. His favourites were the Big bands and their fronting singers. If Mom and Dad were out, Maurice would turn on the radio and accompany the popular swing music, banging on Mom's 'spare buttons' tin with a couple of pieces of cutlery. His ambition was to join the Royal Navy, which he did. Save up and buy a drum kit, learn how to play the things properly and become a dance-band drummer, which he didn't.

The only other big change at home, was that the air-raid shelter had been moved into the 'L' shaped kitchen, allowing the main room (lounge) to be used for a 'knees up.' Yes! London wasn't the only place in Great Britain that knew how to throw an impromptu party, although from the newsreels, one would think everything happened in London. Any good news, and there hadn't been much of that for the first three years of the war, was welcomed in homes up and down the land with a celebratory 'after hours' drink in someone's home, just as long as there was a piano there, or a wind up gramophone. The men would carry the beer home from the pub, plus a few 'borrowed' glasses and the ladies would 'pool' some resources of 'marg', cheese, ham or 'spam', even fishpaste. It didn't matter much. Later, the guests would happily make their way home, singing, laughing and navigating in the blackout. The hosts would tidy up, not worry about taking the piano back until the next day, and go to bed. Just another day!

Dicky's Mom had asked about Mr and Mrs Roe's likes and dislikes. She wanted to send them something for Christmas. Dicky couldn't tell her much, except Auntie liked sweets and Uncle smoked 'Black Twist' tobacco, which he bought 2oz at a time from 'Pagetts' the grocers in Hadley End. He knew that Uncle hadn't always been a farmer and miller and that he'd once worked on the railway, as a guard, in Sheffield. A photograph of Uncle in full guards uniform, complete with oil-lamp, hung on the wall in the farmhouse dining room.

Dicky didn't know that Bert Roe and his wife Tilly had moved to Woodmill and lived in the cottage, later inhabited by Mr and Mrs Bull, before moving into the farm in 1919. He also did not know that they could not have children of their own and that they had 'fostered' other children over the years between the wars. During WW2, foster parents of evacuees received ten shillings (50p) per week and an extra eight shillings and sixpence (42p) for each additional child. That was supposed to cover everything including clothes. It's not surprising that there were many subsequent stories of evacuees being made to work for little or nothing. Dicky knew plenty of kids, village locals and evacuees, who worked at home. He did not remember any instance of any one complaining. It was merely a way of life.

The Colour Purple

As usual, the group making their way home from school to Woodmill, consisted of Dicky, young Duggie, Pete Sharratt and his young sister Rosie. Also in the group, before they took a different route to Woodhouses, were Bob Mewis, sometimes his sister Jean, a few other kids from Woodhouses and always the pretty Fisk girls, Rita and Kathy.

There was never any urgency, certainly never any school homework, seemingly unheard of at Yoxall. Most kids had some sort of chore to help with in their homes which, without services such as water on tap, electricity, gas or mains sewage, meant there was always firewood to chop or collect, coal or coke to fetch in, water to fetch from the pump, oil lamps to see to, livestock to feed.

Apart from the many farms, almost everyone had a few chickens and sometimes a pig, in their back garden to supplement the vegetables that everyone grew in every spare bit of ground. Wartime rationing was a big problem for town and city dwellers, but not for most country folk who were natural self-providers. Those that weren't, such as professional people, tradesmen, recently arrived townspeople, were always able to find someone local who could provide basic home produced essentials at a small cost.

They meandered along the winding tarmac and loose stoned road. No footpaths, high hedges both sides, an occasional gateway to one of the many fields being the only place to evade the increasing army traffic of mainly American troops. For the first half of the journey the older kids would be vigilant. In the absence of any traffic noise and other sounds associated with town and city life, it was easy to hear the sound of approaching army trucks and to take evasive action. The rest of the way home was easier, with wide natural grass verges and stretches of common land, a favourite place for one of the many games they played, usually involving chasing the Fisk girls.

Sometimes an American soldier would toss out a few sweets in response to their cries of "got any gum, chum!" Sometimes the trucks would contain only coloured soldiers, the first coloured people most kids had ever seen, apart from those in American movies.

One day, as the group strolled round one of the many bends, they saw one of the army trucks parked off the road near some bushes. All the soldiers were coloured. Some were smoking, some were drinking out of tin cups and all were chattering and laughing excitedly. As the group passed, quietly and shyly acknowledging the friendly 'hiya toots' and big grins, a couple of soldiers emerged from the bushes, doing up the fly buttons of their uniform trousers.

"They've bin forra piss," whispered Pete Sharratt and they all giggled.

"I wonder if they are black all over," whispered another.

"I'm going to have a look" said one of the girls and, waiting until they had got round the next bend, got off the road and disappeared into the bushes. Within a few minutes, her face flushed and giggling, she was back.

"It's black with a purple end" she screamed excitedly and repeated it whilst skipping down the road. "It's black with a purple end. It's black with a purple end, ee, I, ee, I, it's black with a purple end." They all took up the chant as they continued homewards.

In a large group, the coloured American servicemen were noisy, always shrieking and laughing. In small groups of two or three, they were shy and giggly. On the other hand, most white American servicemen were self confident and cheeky. They would often say "Have you got an older sister as cute as you?" or, "my name is so and so and I sure am lonely," or, "where's the nightlife around here."

All American servicemen however, were generous, good fun and objects of great curiosity to everyone in and around Yoxall.

The Look, Duck and Vanish Brigade

Much to the annoyance of the members, that was the popular name given to the local L.D.V. (local defence volunteer) branch, the early forerunner of the Home Guard and commanded, quite naturally, by the captain of the village cricket team, Alf 'Pop' Lester, who also owned Lesters Garage. Despite his small stature, 'Pop' was a force to be reckoned with and the sight of him, large bushy moustache bristling, marching and controlling his group of steadfast, highly trained killers brandishing their various implements of war, farm tools, palings and about four WW1 Royal Enfield rifles, no bullets, would have struck the same sort of fear and terror in the enemy, as was felt by any visiting cricket team facing 'Pop's' deadly 'leg breaks'.

For a long time Pop's fighting men were poorly equipped, but that didn't deter 'Pop'. Under his knowledgeable tuition at Longcroft Hall, H.Q. for Yoxall Platoon, the bulk of his force became 'highly trained' despatch riders, despite having only one old serviceable army motorbike. The lack of petrol, due to rationing, did not deter 'Pop' Lester, who commanded his team of would-be despatch riders, none of whom held any sort of driving licence, to take it in turns to physically push the bike to the top of the training field hill, mount the 'perishin' thing and freewheel back down the hill, to get used to staying on and guiding it. "It is essential to be ready and despite any emergency, by God we will be!" one could imagine 'Pop' saying to any critic.

Unlike today, this was a time when ownership of any form of motor transport was rare indeed and was probably about one person in a thousand, especially so in rural areas, where the few tractor drivers could not necessarily drive a car and certainly would not be able to afford one.

Car owners, in class conscious Britain, would include wealthy business owners, the upper class, some professionals, a few headmasters, business representatives, travelling salesmen, but no 'working class' apart from a few motorbike owners. Even international footballers on their 'fixed maximum wage' had second jobs to supplement their basic wage, plus £2 win bonus extra and were no better off financially than a factory worker promoted to shift supervisor.

The war would change all that and few returning servicemen would want to settle for what was previously 'their lot'.

As the war progressed, essential equipment filtered through to 'Pop' Lester's men, now formally titled the Home Guard and more realistic training methods were introduced. Night-time field manoeuvres were organised, in which American troops stationed at Sudbury were used. On one occasion half of 'Pop' Lester's men were sent out to ambush the attacking coloured American troops, while the remainder stayed guarding the 'Yanks' objective, HQ at Longcroft Hall.

The Yankee troops easily evaded 'Pop Lester's men and captured HQ without much difficulty. They secured the platoon and ate the supper meant for the successful Home Guard, who, confused and fed up, could only watch them.

"I'll be buggered! fancy askin' us to fate darkies in the middle of the nate! If they didna open theer eyes, how'd we be able to see 'em?" said private Raworth to 'Pop Lester's son, Corporal Jack Lester later.

Total volunteers in the UK for the Home Guard exceeded 1.5 million. The age limit was 65 years, but many 70 and 80 year olds managed to take part.

Alfred 'Pop' Lester

It would be improper to write any sort of book referring to Yoxall, without a respectful acknowledgement of one of Yoxall's favourite characters.

Alfred Lester was born in penury in 1870, the first son of a young destitute girl. Whatever genetic gifts his mother bestowed on young Alfred were soon to be presented and reinforced by a remarkable aptitude for survival, enthusiasm and determination to understand and conquer anything mechanical or sporting.

Alf left school at 14, became apprenticed to the local blacksmith at 4/6d (22p) per week and started playing cricket for the village team the same year, in the match that saw him bowled out first ball. Alf's lifelong love affair with cricket had begun.

Alf's apprenticeship would be 'hands on' practical from the very first day. No libraries or text books of technical information. No technically qualified instructon. No TV or films of any kind. From the very start it would be learning from the basic 'get it red 'ot fust, then 'it it wi' the ammer' style of learning any craft. The necessary skill would follow from long hours of working the metal to whatever shape was required, 10 hours a day, 6 days a week. The norm for a working man. Sunday was church, cricket, any other sport or pigeons.

Perhaps that steady learning, experimenting, bashing and shaping of metal forged the man himself. He'd proved it with metal. He knew he was capable of changing and shaping. He knew it required patience, but what he probably didn't realise was that he'd also collected a general wisdom of approach to the everyday difficulties of life and a sense of humour to go with it.

Perhaps learning to be village blacksmith should be included in every child's curriculum and every potential politician's also.

Having mastered the art of working with metal, he added wheelwrighting and carpentry to his growing range of skills, soon set up his own 'smithy' and started experimenting with and repairing the 'new fangled' bicycles. It took him a whole Sunday afternoon to master the repair of a pneumatic tyre. No cricket match then!

Alf and his brother-in-law set up Yoxall's first garage and built a car, assembling the bought spare parts in their workshop. It worked fine, except for the fact that it had one forward gear and two reverse.

Along the way, at the age of 25, Alf married Mary Wright, a local girl and they produced and raised 10 children in the old schoolhouse, later to become his first workshop. Two of their sons would die in the First World War.

'Pop' Lester's skills eventually embraced many ancient and modern crafts and at the age of 85, with no intention of retiring, he would be working with electrically powered tools. He was also still playing cricket, despite two of his sons, Jack and young Alf, having retired from the game.

'Pop' Lester's cricket career lasted 75 years and he achieved national fame as England's oldest cricketer. In the opinion of many, he was the working man's Dr W G Grace.

He was also a founder member of the Yoxall and District Rifle Club. The eyes and hands that enabled him to achieve so much with any material also made him a 'crack shot'. At the age of 79, on the disbanding of the Home Guard, he won the final shooting competition at a range of 600 yards. His score was 45 out of a possible 50.

He had a remarkable life and a remarkable wife, of whom not enough is known.

'Pop' Lester died at home on June 30th 1964. He was 94 and finally 'out'.

Alfred 'Pop' Lester

The Milk Run

Like all other dairy farms, large and small, the milk, provided by Uncle Bert's cows, was put through a cooling system, similar to which every dairy farmer had. It was then put into 10gallon metal 'churns', which were collected from each farm every day by large, flat-back, trucks and transported to Midland Counties Dairies, Birmingham. There it would be treated, bottled and distributed throughout the Midlands by their own fleet of small delivery vans. Plastic containers, supermarkets and motorways were still a long way off.

Jack, the driver of the truck collecting from the local farms, would swap news with Uncle Bert whilst loading and securing the full churns with steel chains. He would leave clean empty churns in place of the full ones and after a smoke, and a drink from his bottle, take his full load to the Birmingham dairy, unload and load up with clean empty churns, ready for the next day's, eighty mile round, trip.

Uncle, who was aware of Dicky's desire to somehow, get his bike from Yardley Wood, had an idea. If someone in Dicky's family could get his bike to the dairy, perhaps Jack could be persuaded to fetch it over on his milk lorry. Jack was agreeable to the idea, but not to involve the company he worked for. Any private arrangements of that nature, and apparently there were many, had to be without the consent and knowledge of Midland Counties Dairies. An emergency service in times of great difficulties, so to speak. And worth a packet of 'fags' to the driver, the favourite 'currency' of the day. This was just one example of the 'power and opportunism' most drivers of commercial transport had, during the war and immediate post-war years. Absolutely essential to the rapid growth of the Black-market and 'spivery'.

The big snag in all this was organising it. Not many people had telephones in the house. Certainly not council house dwellers and small farms. The nearest telephone box to the Blood household was in Ravenshill Rd, about 400yds away and there just wasn't one anywhere near the farm. So any arrangements made by post would take weeks.

Jack, the milk lorry driver, had a better idea. Dicky was to write home, telling his parents that he is coming home for a couple of days and that he is getting a 'lift'. Jack will 'drop' Dicky where he can catch the No 11 Outer Circle bus, which connects the 13a bus route to Yardley Wood. Two days later, he will look out for Dicky at the same spot at an agreed, very early time, Jack's collection schedule and timetable being crucial. Daily fresh milk was a vital commodity in this age before refrigeration. How Dicky would get himself and his bike to the 'pick up' point would be Dicky's problem, and one that didn't worry Dicky, so the letter was sent.

The following Saturday, Jack arrived at Mill Farm, had a smoke and a chat with Uncle Bert, then left, carrying a full churn in exchange for a clean empty one, plus one very enthusiastic Dicky, his first ride in the cab of a truck. The trip was exciting, different and took about 5 hours. At least 3 of which were taken up collecting milk from the rest of the farms on Jack's round, before making their way back to Birmingham. They ate their lunch of sandwiches plus one of Auntie's pasties whilst on the move. The roads were quiet, the main A38 being less of a problem than the narrow, winding, country lanes on which livestock of some kind would often be on the move, on foot! They both drank from their 'pop' bottles of cold tea, thermos flasks being a luxury item and certainly unknown to the 'working class'. Ignorance can be a comfort! Jack dropped Dicky off where the No 11 bus crossed the Tyburn Road and told him to watch out for his lorry the following Monday morning at 7 am. No later!

Everything went off without a hitch. Dicky was home by about 4pm and immediately 'volunteered' to look after Barry and Laurence whilst Dolly Blood did some shopping without the hindrance caused by the kids. That wasn't a problem, as Dicky could tell them about his new found skills as a farmer's boy and wrestling with Marie, the calf. 5 year old Barry had an idea of what Dicky was talking about, but Laurence, barely 3 years old, probably listened because the words sounded so funny.

The rest of the day passed quite normally. The usual family stuff, exchanging stories and questions about Dicky's new billeting. Any chance of Duggie visiting etc, and catching up with Dicky's pals that evening.

Sunday morning, and Dicky was up before anyone else, probably out of habit as everyone was always up early at Woodmill. He rescued his bike from under the old piece of barrage balloon that was protecting it from the ravages of the British climate and inspected it with dismay. Both tyres were flat, the frame was showing many signs of rust and it was covered in cobwebs and dust. Dicky cleaned the bike up, as best he could and inflated the tyres, which to his surprise stayed inflated. He went for a ride around the area, satisfied himself that the bike was rideable, then announced that he would start out the following morning at 5 am. He could not, must not be late, or Jack would assume he wasn't coming and not wait more than a couple of minutes. He had another evening with his pals in the road outside, swapping stories and the like. Then it was off to bed and up, ready for another exciting instalment in *'this young explorer's quest to find the, long lost, secret route, known only to the Ancient Briton scouts, who helped to hide the marauding bands of fighting men, constantly harassing the marching columns of, better disciplined and armed, Roman Legionnaires'.*

He eventually decided to follow the 13a bus route until where the No.11 bus route crossed. Then follow that to Tyburn Road, where he would meet Jack.

He said goodbye to his Mom, the only other person in the Blood family up and about. No kiss or a hug, not that Dicky minded. Anyway, he would have wondered what was up! Many years later, he would wonder why there was never that sort of closeness in the family. Sure they were close. Sure they would always look out for each other and, if need be, fight for each other. But hugs and kisses? Nah!

Apart from early and late shift workers travelling to and from their place of work, mainly on bikes, there were a few trucks, some presumably heading for Smithfield Wholesale Market, where just about every sort of provision, consumable or not, would be sold to retailers from all parts of Birmingham. Horse-drawn carts also would be about, although this type of transport was rapidly giving way to petrol driven horsepower. Dicky was amazed how quickly things seemed to be changing and as he pedalled the time away, he was constantly surprised as the slumbering City of Birmingham suddenly awakened with a rush and crackle of latent energy, as it emerged from its much needed rest. It was as if every side street had just released them, as by 6.30 every main road seemed to be full of cycles and buses carrying workers to the factories, many of which were on the route Dicky was making his way along.

Then, calamity! Dicky, his eyes everywhere trying to take in the panoramic tumultuous activity, so completely different to his slow peaceful life at Woodmill, didn't see one of the many potholes in the much neglected road. It was a deep one that not only fetched Dicky off his bike, but also slightly buckled the front wheel and punctured the inner tube. Dicky was horrified. He wasn't sure how much further it was to Tyburn Road, but he knew he had no choice, but to take the weight of the front wheel off the ground and wheel it as best and as fast as he could. As he'd cycled past one of the big factories, could have been 'Fisher and Ludlow's', he'd noticed the outside wall clock. It was twenty minutes to seven, and that was about five minutes ago. Holding the front of the bike up, he walked and jogged as fast as he could along the footpath, dodging around the scurrying workers intent on 'clocking in' on time. Eventually, hot and flustered, he got to Tyburn Road, crossed over to the appointed 'pick-up' point, dropped the bike and sat down on the grass verge. What was the time! He asked a couple of running workers. Talk about 'beat the clock'. One of them shouted "Quarter past seven kid."

Two years later, when he started work, he found out that if a factory worker was 16 minutes late, that worker would lose 30 minutes pay. No wonder they were running!

Dicky was dismayed. What now? The more he thought about it, the more the obvious thing to do, was carry on. It would be difficult to make his way back to where he wouldn't be expected and probably easier to scrounge a lift from one of the many trucks going towards where he was expected. And he knew the drill, except he hadn't got any 'fags'! Content with the plan, basic as it was, he settled down on the grassy verge, eating the sandwiches Dolly Blood had prepared for him. He stuck out his thumb a few times, but soon realised that the drivers were too intent on avoiding the mass of cyclists on the roads, to notice his thumb. Eight o'clock arrived and the mass of cyclists vanished, as if by magic. Within the space of two minutes the pedalling throngs had dwindled to one or two and the roads were now the domain of trucks, vans and empty buses.

Dicky now stood up and holding up the damaged cycle for all to see, stuck out his left arm, thumb outstretched.

He didn't have long to wait. A small truck pulled in and an arm beckoned from the nearside window. As Dicky approached, carrying the front end of his bike, the owner of the arm opened his door and jumped out.

"E'yar kid! Give us that 'ere!" He picked the bike up and put it into the back of the truck, laying it across the top of the many wrapped, similarly shaped, parcels. "It's OK. It won't 'urt them any. They're tools and other stuff for the RAF at Fradley."

This much older and bigger lad then motioned to Dicky to sit between the driver, a much older man, and himself. An old cushion of sorts was already on the engine cover. Presumably, hitchhikers were welcome. The lad introduced himself.

"My name's 'arry and this is me Dad. 'Is name is 'arry as well, so I 'as to call 'im Dad, or I'll think I'm talkin' to me self." He laughed, Dicky grinned and the old man shrugged his shoulders.

"Where're you off to sonny?"

Dicky explained his predicament and asked if they were going anywhere near Yoxall.

Old 'arry said, "That's the other side of Lichfield, innit?"

"Yeah!" said Dicky excitedly. It was the first time Dicky had met anyone from Birmingham, apart from those involved in the evacuation, who'd actually heard of Yoxall.

"'Ow we gooin' to find it without signposts?" enquired young 'arry.

"We ain't gooin' to worry about that now" replied his Dad.

"We'll ask when we get to Lichfield."

"If we're going to Lichfield, I know the way from there. I even know the way from here." Dicky grinned and continued, "I inna got any fags but if you take me all the way, I reckon Auntie will give you a pasty each."

The two 'arrys looked at each other. Rather glumly, Dicky thought. The father put the vehicle in gear, released the handbrake and pulled away from the grassy verge. As the truck picked up speed he said to the windscreen, "we got a right one 'ere! Fust 'e tells us 'e ain't got no fags, then 'e tries to bribe us with pasties. I dunno what the worlds cummin' to. What do you reckon 'arry?"

The younger 'arry had got a serious look on his face and turned round to gaze steadily at Dicky for a long minute or two. He shook his head slowly and said "Well, I dunno! 'e could be a spy. Seems funny that 'e should be there, as if waitin' forrus. Especially as we're carrying them new, secret, special, weapons for the planes at Fradley."

He made long deliberate pauses as he emphasised his words. Older 'arry, looking straight ahead, pursed his lips and said. "I've got a feeling you could be right there son! Problem is, what do we do with'im? 'and 'im over to the police? Or the RAF? Or shall we tek care of 'im ourselves?"

Dicky was alarmed. He couldn't get out from between them, especially as the truck was travelling at a good steady pace. He'd never met them before. Perhaps they were spies, or secret agents carrying explosives to sabotage wherever they were going. They must be well trained because they both spoke perfect English, well, sort of.

"I inna a spy!" he blurted out. "I'm only 12 and too small anyway!"

The older 'arry chuckled and said, "you're as big as that Herr Goebbels fella, an' 'e's poison!"

Young 'arry couldn't contain himself any longer. He burst out laughing, ruffled Dicky's mop and chortled, "got you gooin' there mate, shudda sin your face!" They laughed some more, Dicky as well, mightily relieved.

Soon they reached Lichfield and when Dicky realised they were still on the road to Yoxall, he was able to tell them that Woodmill was only about another 6 miles or thereabouts.

"Okay by us kid! As long as we get back to our firm before 4 o'clock this arternoon, we're alright. An' we'll do that easy."

Their truck trundled down Mill Farm drive, wildly exciting Nellie and surprising Uncle, who wasn't expecting Dicky for another hour yet. Explanations and pleasantries were exchanged and mugs of tea consumed by all, before the 'arry duo left to deliver their important parcels to Fradley Aerodrome, officially known as RAF Lichfield. [3]

The Reality of Flying a Night Bomber

"Anyone whose sole experience of flying is confined to holiday jets has simply no idea of what it was like to fly in a wartime bomber.

The numbing cold, with icy winds seeking out the chinks in one's clothing, the shattering noise, the constant teeth jarring vibration, the turbulence causing the whole airframe to flex and creak; having to wear an oxygen mask which made even breath reek of wet rubber; the cramp, which the tight harness made it impossible to relieve..."

Air Commodore Cozens recalling his time flying Wellington bombers in 1943.

[3] RAF Lichfield
There were approximately 3500 RAF personnel at RAF Lichfield during the war, mainly RAF aircrew in training. These were mostly from the Commonwealth and in particular Australia. Here they trained on Wellington bombers. The airfield became so busy (114,000 movements from December 42 to June 45) that it became necessary to use other satellite airfields such as the one at Church Broughton, to satisfy training commitments. In May 1942, the first Operational Bombing Missions were flown, as part of the 1000 bomber raid to Cologne, one of the raids which, many, many years later, brought much unjustified criticism on the head of 'Bomber' Harris, the Supreme Commander of RAF Bomber Command. Veterans, of course, will remember who started 'blitzing' major cities in Britain and Europe, which left hundreds of thousands dead, many hundreds of thousands injured and homeless, including the 60,595 UK civilians who died as a result of German air raids. See 'Bomber Harris' by Henry Probert or www.greenhillbooks.com

"Jump off 'Moss', or you'll go Under"

"Let's 'ave a look at y' bike then," said Uncle, as the truck containing the two 'arrys made it's way down the drive to continue their delivery to RAF Lichfield. With a practised skill, garnered from the many years of maintaining his old upright, 'special' constable's, Raleigh bicycle, the only piece of mechanical transport he was ever going to possess, Uncle Bert quickly removed the damaged wheel from the frame. With the aid of two old steel serving spoons that had not seen a dining table for many years, he levered off one side of the tyre, enabling him to pull out the damaged inner tube.

"Get us a bucket of watter lad! an I'll show y' how to mend a puncture," he muttered.

Dicky galloped off and by the time he'd returned with the water, Uncle had removed the valve retaining nut, completely removed the inner tube from the wheel, re-assembled the valve and was blowing the inner tube up, with the aid of his own bicycle pump, Dicky never having owned one.

"Right! Dicky lad. Grab 'old of about six inches of this tube between y'two 'ands and work it round under the watter. When y'see bubbles, put a ring round the 'ole the bubbles are comin' from wi' this blue pencil."

He took out the blue pencil from the open drawer in his home-made work-bench and laid it alongside the yellow 'Dunlop' tin containing the puncture repair kit. Dicky pushed his old jumper sleeves up above his elbows and proceeded to do as he was instructed.

Soon he could see two trails of bubbles making their way to the surface from two holes about one inch apart.

"I can see them! I can see them!" yelled Dicky, lifting out the tube and quickly marking two rings as instructed.

Uncle wiped dry the area around the two marked holes and with the same piece of old cloth, 'fanned' away a clear spot on the dusty bench top. He then lay that part of the tube on the bench and secured it in place with two, strategically placed old two pound weights. Hardly pausing, he rummaged in his capacious pocket for his box of

'England's Glory' matches and 'roughed up' the surface of the inner tube marked with blue pencil. Blowing away any loose particles, he then selected two patches from the repair tin and gave them to Dicky saying, "Right! Youm got nimble little fingers. Get the backin' of'n these patches an' stand ready."

From the same tin, he then produced a small tube of glue and sparingly applied it to the repair area, before straightening up, putting his hands behind his back and taking a long deep breath whilst arching his back. "We'll gie' that a couple of minutes to get tacky, then y'can stick the patches on. Mek sure y'gets them over the 'oles proper."

After a suitable pause, during which Uncle tried the glued area for 'tackiness', Dicky was allowed to firmly affix the patches and Uncle, from another small tin, sprinkled white powdery stuff on and around them.

"French chalk lad! Stops the tube stickin' to the inside of the tyre." He then covered the area with the cloth, put a piece of flat wood on top and added another, heavier, weight on top of that, "We'll gie'it a few more minutes to mek sure it's set, 'cause we'm got to put it in the watter agin to check for any more 'oles".

No more punctures were found and after Uncle straightened the buckled wheel with a few judicious taps with a hammer and some work with a spoke key, the front wheel was returned to its proper shape, more or less.

"It inna perfect, but no wuss than the back wheel," remarked Uncle as he watched Dicky riding the bike round and round the yard whilst he contentedly tried to get a 'good un goin' with his pipe and 'baccy'.

It wasn't long before another, much larger truck made its noisy way down the hill and pulled up at the end of the drive. It was the milk lorry and a very surprised Jack when he saw Dicky cycling up the farm driveway, followed by the madly barking Nellie and a sedately paced Uncle. More explanations and time for another mug of tea.

"Dunna walk down. Bring y'truck. It'll save y'ten minutes," said Uncle.

"O'ar!" replied Jack. "An' the milk will 'ave started turnin' to bleedin' butter before I get back on the road again! No thanks, I'll walk. I need to stretch me legs a bit anyway."

Normality returned to Mill Farm after Jack had left with his lorry load of milk destined for Birmingham, and after a sandwich, Dicky explained to Auntie and Uncle the plan he and his older brother had conceived. Maurice or rather 'Moss', as all his pals in Birmingham called him, had never visited the farm, or indeed Yoxall. He'd suggested cycling to Lichfield on the first convenient Saturday, where Dicky would be waiting to meet him and cycle together to Woodmill, where he would stay the night and cycle back home next day. If Moss didn't get a postcard to the contrary, he was to assume the next Saturday was alright and set out about 7 am, arriving at Lichfield about 9.30am, where Dicky of course, would be waiting ready to accompany Moss the seven miles back to Woodmill.

The arrangement was acceptable to both of them and Auntie reminded Dicky that Moss would have to share his bed, which wasn't a problem to Dicky as no one in the Blood household had ever had a bed to themselves.

The plan went, well, according to plan and Dicky and Maurice were back at the farm in time for the midday sandwich and a cup tea, after which, just like all boys, they were up and out.

Dicky, keen to show off his 'territory', took Maurice to the river where, if you were still and patient, you could see the brown trout and catch the slow moving 'crawfish' by hand. He showed him how to sit quietly down-wind of the rabbit warren and watch as the little ones emerged, twitching noses uppermost. Took him through fields of cattle, which caused Maurice to question Dicky's judgement. Maurice knew what cattle were and he'd certainly seen comic strips whereby someone is being chased by a ferocious bull, but he'd never been close to, or even in the same field with either before.

Even though he was much taller and bigger than Dicky, he kept close as they walked through the disinterested cattle, his eyes swivelling this way and that in search of a bull or a threatening cow. Dicky loved it and said, "If you think these are scary, wait until tonight when you'll see something really scary."

Dicky, of course, was thinking about the owl, but despite being pressed for more information, refused to enlighten Maurice further, instead he said, "Wait till you see the mill and walk the big wheel."

They made their way back to the farm, each of them successfully jumping the winding river at one of the narrower parts and raced each other across the bottom meadow, 12 year old Dicky struggling to match the pace of 14 year old Maurice. Breathless and laughing, they both leaned on the fence, where they were soon found by Nellie practically going crackers, her natural assumption being that she now had two pals to play with.

"C'mon then 'Moss', I'll show you the mill and how it works," shouted Dicky excitedly in the sure knowledge that he was about to impress Maurice with his ability to operate everything in the mill building. Dicky, with some haste, made his way towards, what appeared to Maurice, a very old 'L' shaped farm cottage built into the bank of the high ground behind it. Lifting the latch and opening the middle door, Dicky entered and nimbly skipped down the steps into the gloom of the window-less building. Maurice, being much taller and a stranger to this new and even stranger environment, cautiously made his way down the steps, his eyes and brain taking in and trying to register the seemingly complex mass of basic structures of timber. Flour (rough ground) collection box, from which the supply chute extended upwards and through to the next floor. Hanging chain which appeared to go upwards forever through split, upward opening trapdoors, a very long handled iron lever, which also seemed to go through to the floor above. A hanging rope, which he learned later was the 'clutch' rope used to operate the 'lifting' chain. Massive platform scales, for weighing the ground corn after it was bagged. Stacked empty 'used' sacks. Rolls of baling twine. Various pieces of 'useful' odds and ends to do with milling, either hanging on great iron wall hooks, or stacked in corners out of the way. All this in the bottom floor of the timber-framed building with its massive, upper floor, support cross-beams.

Gazing round, Maurice realised that what appeared to be a very thick layer of dust, was in fact flour dust. In the corners of all the timber structures, this flour dust had collected and formed deposits up to nearly an inch deep. This dust coated everything that wasn't walked on and showed up the tracks and droppings left by resident rats and mice. Maurice climbed the wooden steps to the next floor where Dicky showed him the mounted grindstones in their timber, sectionally constructed, housing at the top of the chute leading to the collection box on the ground floor. Took him up to the top floor where there was only room for a wooden hopper into which the unmilled corn, just raised from below on the end of the chain was tipped. Back down to the middle floor to show him the loading door, which opened outwards over the yard, at the height used for centuries to unload the horse drawn carts. Opposite this door and behind the grindstones housing was an opening in the brick wall, over which could be seen the top of the giant water wheel, which when turning, provided the necessary power for milling and for lifting sacks of corn etc. It was a cold, inhospitable place, even in summer, as it was now. Little light. No movement. The only sound was the constant dripping trickle of water wriggling its way through the imperfect seal of the closed sluice gate above the big wheel and splashing onto the paddles.

As the boys looked over the wall and down at the wheel, Dicky exclaimed triumphantly, "I can walk that wheel round, inside it or outside it."

Maurice took up the challenge, "If you can do it, I can do it, but 'ow do we get to it?"

Dicky, grinning delightedly, shouting, "this way to the big wheel" and scampered across the floor and down the steps into the farmyard.

Maurice, not so familiar with the surroundings, following more slowly, as Dicky, once Maurice had appeared, scampered to the end of the mill building, round the back, over a two plank width bridge which spanned the 'mill race' and opened a timber door revealing the big wheel, the hub and axle of which were level with the top of the brick built pit it sat in. The wheel was a little over a metre wide and the pit wide enough for the wheel to turn freely. At the bottom of the pit, Maurice could see the mill stream trickling by, under and through the archway to join the main stream outside. When the mill was in operation, driven by the deluge of water released by the raised sluice gate, this little mill stream became a furiously gushing torrent, hence the term 'mill-race'.

Now, of course, it was still and Dicky had already clambered down, between the giant spokes and was standing inside the wheel.

"Come on Moss!" Maurice, needing no second invitation, quickly joined him and copying Dicky, soon had the wheel turning, slowly and ponderously.

"Crikey! What would we do now if the farmer or someone else turned the water on?" asked Maurice, not really wanting to hear the answer.

"It's alright. There's not enough water up there. The gate along the field 'as to be shut for about a day to build up enough water. I'll show you later."

They stopped putting any effort into walking the wheel and it slowly came to a stop, enabling them both to climb out. Dicky then stepped onto the paddles on the outside of the wheel and tried to get it moving, which it did but quite slowly. He then got off and said "come on Moss, you 'ave a go."

Maurice, now confident, climbed on the wheel and tried to get it going, which it did, but again slowly.

"I'll get on as well," said Dicky clambering alongside his brother, "together, it should be easier."

The big wheel started to gain speed from the extra impetus and soon it became very obvious that it would keep increasing speed unless one or both got off. Dicky, being nearest to the low accessible side, immediately stepped off, but Maurice, being on the side next to the brick wall, over which they'd both previously looked down at the wheel, first had to sidle across whilst maintaining his footing on the slippery wooden paddles. As he did this, they both realised the wheel was still increasing speed and now going faster than Maurice, now white-faced, could keep up with. Dicky would never forget the sight of his older brother's, now very concerned white features, as they slowly followed his furiously stepping feet into the abyss.

"Jump off Moss! Or you'll go under the wheel!" yelled Dicky, followed by the splash as Maurice hit the water. Dicky looked down, saw that Maurice was clear of the still turning wheel and paddling towards the low brick built archway, through which he soon emerged, socks and footwear wet, grinning, but still a bit pale.

"I've got to help milk the cows soon" said Dicky as Maurice laid his socks and boots along the top of the wall in the sun, to hopefully dry. "D'you want to 'ave a go?"

Maurice looked at him and said, "I ain't goin' anywhere near any cow. I don't like the slow way they look at you, as if trying to chose the best place to kick you or stick their horns."

They both grinned, Maurice no doubt with a sense of relief and wondering how he was going to describe his 'big wheel' adventure to his pals in 'Brum' later that day after cycling the thirty miles home after tea. No problem to a fifteen year old boy who'd been cycling regularly since the age of twelve. Dicky felt, well triumphal!

Which was just as well, because the expected scary night with the bedroom owl proved to be an anticlimax. There was no moonlight!

Maurice was surprised to learn that Uncle Bert and Dicky had already milked the cows, put them out to graze, cleaned the cowshed and were back in the farmhouse for breakfast, before he got up. "Blimey!" he said, "I only got up because the bl...!"

Dicky's well shod foot clattered into his shin. "ouch!" Maurice yelped, suddenly remembering Dicky's advice the previous day about swearing.

"The er hens were mekin' such a racket, I thought it must be time to get up. I don't usually get up before 10 o'clock on Sundays."

"Aye, well youm up now lad, an' just in time for a nice farm breakfast. That's, of course, youm a wantin' it!"

Auntie turned back to the fire, over which was the massive frying pan containing about a dozen rashers of bacon. Uncle passed one of the filled mugs of tea to Maurice saying with a chuckle "I 'opes youm brought y'own sugar!"

"Dunna tek any notice of 'im Maurice or e'l get wuss!" exclaimed Auntie, as with a practised hand she transferred the cooked bacon to a warmed tin before breaking seven eggs into the hot fat of the pan. "Two each for you allus 'ungry lot and one for me, cos that's all I can manage."

She placed the eggs on the, now waiting, plates of bacon and passed them to the table before frying the, already cut, pieces of bread and dishing them up. Dicky and Maurice, both enthusiastically tucking in, exchanged meaningful glances. Dicky had boasted several times about Uncle's prodigious ability at spitting and

Maurice hadn't been convinced. The bedroom owl had been a failure. Surely Uncle wouldn't also let him down.

Dicky had no cause to worry. The meal finished, Uncle, as usual, swung his chair round, got out his pipe, knife and stick of tobacco and commenced the ritual he didn't even have to think about. Maurice was fascinated. Sure, there were pipe smokers in Birmingham, but he'd never seen any stick tobacco before and when Uncle Bert leaned forward to light a spill from the spill container in the hearth, then proceed to light his pipe, a major operation in itself, he was engrossed. The sucking and puffing, the 'tamping down' with his thumb of red hot bits of 'baccy' trying to erupt like a miniature volcano. The clouds of swirling blue smoke. Maurice was impressed, and Uncle hadn't spit yet! Twice he leaned forward as if to send a stream of expectorates towards the fire and twice he leaned back with a little contented smile on his face. He knew what they were waiting for! Dicky fidgeted and was just about to say something when, at last, Uncle leaned forward again and released a powerful jet of brown spit right into the heart of the fire.

"Eh! Did y'see that by any chance? Did you 'appen to be lookin'? Not a drop spilt! I maun be getting' better." Uncle chuckled. He knew he'd impressed the boys and he loved showing off.

After breakfast, Maurice set off on his 30 mile cycle ride back home, Dicky accompanying him as far as Lichfield.

The Mating Game

The milking had been done and Dicky was unchaining the cows so that he could herd them to one of the fields for the day. There was no great hurry as it was Saturday and no school.

"Leave May chained up for a while" said Uncle, already busy sweeping the milking shed prior to throwing several buckets of water down before a final sweep out.

All straw and muck was shovelled into a wheelbarrow and taken the thirty yards or so to the muckheap. There it would be added to, every 'mucking out', which was twice daily. This growing heap of muck would also include pig muck and would be left to' rot down' before being spread by horse and cart around the fields once yearly.

In the right condition, this muck would be an ideal breeding ground for worms and in the early summer, Uncle would occasionally lift a crust of hardened manure with a garden fork. If there were signs of worms breeding he would mutter "aye' theers a rate good bit o' muck theer me lad" and put the crust back. If there were no signs of life he would say, "aye, a bit too cold, I reckon it'll be a few wiks yet."

On this particular day Dicky made sure the cows were in the pre-destined field, shut the gate, wandered back for breakfast and casually asked Uncle why he'd wanted May left in the shed.

"Cos she's gooin' a'courtin', that's why" replied Uncle, hungrily getting his face around a forkful of bacon, egg and fried bread, the fat from which was trickling down his ruddy, unshaven chin.

"'Er milk's dryin' up, she knows it and I knows it. She also knows it's time to go with the bull, 'cos she feels like it. You've seen 'er trying to get a piggyback on the other cows, which looks a bit funny, well that's a cow's way of letting us know. They inna so daft as they look."

Uncle paused to swallow the last remnants of the mouthful of food he had when he started to explain and chew at the same time, then triumphantly continued. "We inna got a bull, but I knows where there is one."

He paused, his concentration now fully on the pieces of egg, bacon and fried bread he was methodically spearing with his fork until it was loaded to his satisfaction. With the loaded fork within inches of his mouth, he continued again. "An' you, Dicky boy, is gunna get some important larnin', 'cos you is gunna tek May up to the big farm on 'top road' and make sure she gets in the yard an' you shuts the gate."

Dicky said nothing and got on with his breakfast. He looked at Auntie. She gave him a smile and continued her meal. The only sound was the 'clickety click' of her teeth, the 'cluck, clucking' of the successful egg layers in the orchard and the steady low whistle of the ever-ready kettle suspended over the fire, which was always alight, whatever the season. Even Nellie was quiet, patiently waiting for the scrap of bacon she knew was coming. "What do I do then?" asked Dicky.

Auntie was choking on a giggle at his innocent question and Uncle was laughing and trying to cope with the forkful of food, now in his mouth, at the same time. Wiping his eyes, face and around his mouth, he chortled, "Dinna worry y'sen boy. Jus get May there safely an' in the yard an' your job's done. All you 'as to do then is tell the farmer that May is in the yard waitin' for 'is bull. Y' can watch, if youm a mind to, but dunna ask me any fool questions 'bout how babies are made. We inna got any kids, but it all seems fairly simple to me."

Dicky looked again at Auntie. She wasn't smiling now and was suddenly busy filling the teapot for a second mug of tea for Uncle. Sensing it wasn't the time for the sort of questions he knew he would have difficulty formulating anyway, Dicky finished his breakfast and made his way down the garden path and into the farmyard. He took the precaution, as advised by Uncle, to first go up the public right of way, behind the mill building, to prop open the gate leading to the 'top road'. He certainly didn't fancy following May up the narrow path between the mill wall and the orchard wall and finding the gate closed. May had got long widespread horns and was normally excitable. A dead end would confuse and unsettle her more than she already was and could easily lead to an unintentional, but very nasty accident.

Having satisfactorily made sure the gate would not close, Dicky went back, picked a herding stick from the few always outside the milking parlour, went inside and unchained May. He quickly got himself outside and was in position to guide her towards the path up behind the mill when she emerged from the building. The big red cow, seeing her normal path was blocked by Dicky brandishing a stick, took a hesitant step to the left. Dicky, now quite used to all the cows, just gave her a light tap on the rump and sounded off "gerrup theer!" He tried to make his voice sound gruff and dominant like Uncle's voice. Instead it sounded like most kids of 12 years old.

May obediently moved off up the path and into the grassed lane leading to the 'top road'. As there was no rush, Dicky let her stop now and then to get a few mouthfuls of grass although it was quite plain she was doing it out of habit. She kept looking back at Dicky, tossing her head and giving a plaintive 'moo'. She'd then walk a few paces quickly, turn around to face Dicky and wait until he could practically touch her before she wheeled around and continued.

Eventually the reluctant 'prospective lover' and her herdsman reached the 'top road' and made better progress along to the waiting farmyard with gate already open. May, who'd probably been there before, seeing as Uncle had told him that all the cows had had several calves over the previous few years, went straight in and Dicky shut and fastened the farmyard gate.

As instructed, Dicky then went round to the farmhouse kitchen and knocked the door. A voice boomed out "if that's the lad from Bert Roe's place, come on in an' 'ave a cup o' summat."

Dicky tentatively stepped into the kitchen, his eyes on the look out for the dog he just knew would be around somewhere. He wasn't wrong. Two dogs were skulking round the other side of the kitchen table where the farmer sat studying a notebook. The farmer hadn't given any command to the dogs, but it was clear he was in control.

"Right lad, you've brought the cow an' put 'er in the yard, as yer? Good, ready an' waitin', no doubt."

With a pencil, he put a tick beside an entry in the notebook and continued, "right then lad, go back into the yard, shut the gate behind you an' let the bull out of the cowshed. Just unchain 'im 'an e'll do the rest."

Noticing the expression on Dicky's face, he added "dinna worry 'bout the bull, 'e inna interested in you. 'E will 'ave smelt your cow by now an' will know why she's there. You just unchain 'im an' watch 'im go. When 'e's finished, 'e will go back into the pen where

I'll mek sure there's some fodder forrim. You jus' chain 'im up agin, an' come back an tell me."

"You not coming then?" Dicky enquired, somewhat anxiously.

"Nay lad an' dinna worry yersen. I've told you. The bull 'as got the scent of your cow an' is only interested in'er. Now you just get on with it, I'll be getting' the fodder for when the bull is finished."

Like a man going to the scaffold, Dicky made his way back and into the farmyard, shutting the gate behind him. The split, stable type door to the cowshed was open wide and the bull, Jesus! He looked very big and mean, was snorting and tossing his head up and down, his widespread horns catching and threatening to uproot from the concrete floor the tubular steel frame it was chained to, one of several dividing the length of the shed into equal size stalls. Dicky checked that he could get his body behind the open split door and between it and the wall, hopefully out of sight of the bull, who he reasoned, would come galloping out of the shed once it was released. The bull would have to turn round first of course, because all cattle are normally tethered with their heads forward towards the feedbox and their backsides towards the 6 feet wide by 6 inches deep, easily accessible, gully, the necessary depository for bowel and bladder evacuation of any beasts therein.

Dicky, heart thumping, ventured into the cowshed. He didn't need to imagine he was Tarzan or Flash Gordon or any other comic hero. He felt more like Daniel entering the lion's den and thought perhaps he ought to go to the toilet first. He could see that the chain securing the bull was similar to the chains used on Uncle's farm, with a simple coupling attachment that could be released quickly, but only with the use of two hands. Dicky tried to soothe the bull with a few words and began to hum a tune as Uncle used to do when helping one of his cows to calve, but the bull wasn't interested. It was now steadily pulling against the chain, its head raised high and it's one visible eye glaring backwards at Dicky. It didn't look very co-operative at all and the distance from the doorway to the steel frame, the other side of which was the bull, suddenly seemed much more. Could he make it? What if he slipped and fell? He could imagine himself on the floor, rolling backwards and forwards under the steel barriers, trying to dodge the bull's horns and yelling for the farmer. He managed to stifle the panic rising in him, by practising the swift movement required to get out of the shed and behind the door out of sight of the bull, without slipping. He still hesitated, but instinctively knowing that Uncle Bert wouldn't put him at risk, he approached the bull, both now panting and seemingly aware that something cataclysmic was about to take place.

In one, well rehearsed movement, Dicky slipped the chain and was off like an Olympic sprinter before the bull even moved. From his position behind the split door, which he'd secured to the wall with the ever-present hook, Dicky could hear the scrambling of hooves on the concrete floor of the cowshed. This was immediately followed by the bull emerging at a trot, its head high with flared nostrils sniffing the whereabouts of the source of the 'scent'. May was already on the move as the bull got its bearings and launched itself in her direction. There followed a bizarre chase around the wet cobbles of the farmyard with the bull, sometimes on its two rear legs only, tried to convince May that he was the boy for her. May, being May, was always going to resist to her utmost, whether she wanted him or not, but the bull was an old campaigner who knew his territory well. He eventually cornered May head first into the sharpest corner of the farmyard, mounted her and did what was required of him.

Dicky was impressed. He'd never seen anything like it. He'd seen dogs of course and had an idea what was going on, but these were the days before compulsory sex education at school, so procreation was rarely talked about, except as the butt of schoolboy joking. Conversely, all country kids were well informed, living as they did, on or near livestock farms. Some, living on specialist breeding farms, would be very knowledgeable and go on to careers in that profession. But, because of their isolation from the more frenetic town and city life, they were more naïve in matters of relationships, very shy and easily embarrassed. That was the norm. However, there were notable exceptions and these will be written about later. Dicky stayed hidden while the bull made its leisurely way back to its stall in the shed, whereupon Dicky shut and secured the door. He didn't bother to try and put the chain back around the bull's neck. Even while quietly eating the fodder provided, the bull still looked mean and aware of Dicky's presence and Dicky, of course, still clearly remembered past experiences with bulls.

Seeing the farmer near one of the many buildings bordering the farmyard, Dicky shouted "the bull's back in the stall, but I inna put 'is chain on."

The farmer just nodded. Dicky opened the farm gate and May, waiting close by, cantered through and, tail in the air, made off along the 'top road' at a very impressive speed, thankfully in the right direction. Dicky, only slightly delayed by having to shut the gate, was soon into his 'racing speed mode' but about 50 yards behind and wondering how he was going to get in front of May to 'turn' her into the grassy lane down to her own farm. If he couldn't get past and May continued at this pace, they could both end up in Yoxall village, about 1 mile further on.

Even at his 'Wilson of the Wizard' top racing speed, Dicky was not gaining on May who was sustaining her mad gallop for sanctuary from the rampant bull she obviously hadn't forgotten. Dicky, legs reaching, arms thrashing the air, his mind a maelstrom of crazy thoughts about training May for relay racing and how she would hold and pass the baton, was mightily relieved to see May, without any hesitation, turn right into the grassy lane and continue her headlong dash, now downhill all the way to her own farmyard. Dicky, much relieved, now slowed down to a gentle jog and wasn't surprised to find May alone in her own stall, quietly feeding.

"Job done alright then?" enquired Uncle Bert from the woodshed.

"Yep" replied Dicky.

Over the next few days he thought many times about what he had seen and the questions he somehow couldn't put into words. He even checked May's 'scent', but she smelt exactly the same as all the other cows. He didn't ask about that either!

Jackie Kelly

It was late summer. The fields grass had been cut, turned and the resultant hay collected by the horse-drawn cart. The milking shed, now only housing the cows at milking time for about an hour twice a day, had been scrubbed down, cleaned and the walls white-washed. The hen houses had been cleaned and the lawn scythed, paths weeded, fences creosated. Apart from Dicky, many helping hands of visiting friends and relatives of Mr and Mrs roe had been involved. Cider had been available, but only at the end of the working day and consumed along with ham, pickles and breed supplied by Auntie. The work had been hard, sweaty, but full of humour and banter. It was now quiet. All visitors had left and Uncle suggested that Dicky go home to 'Brum' for a week, which he did with the help of Jack the milk collection driver and his own bike.

As usual Barry and Lawrence were pleased to see him, as was Moss, now working as a plumbers mate, who could now get out with his mates more. Dicky's mom was still working nights at the Austin factory and his dad all day at the B.S.A in the office. Dicky noticed he carreid his sandwiches in a small brown case and was happy to tell any one that he was a Progress Clerk. Very impressive! Nobody knew what a Progress Clerk was, so it sounded good.

The Bentley family nextdoor were absolutely invaluable at this time, having six daughters of whom one was always available to look after Barry and Lawrence. An example of the give and take and help attitude of the war years. Dicky took every chance available to meet up with his pals and make the most of the local facilities, mainly Trittiford Park with its trees, river Cole and boating lake.

Dicky and Johnny Arnold were on Trittiford Park Lake, each in a small rowboat designed and built to hold just one person and very manoeuvrable. At 1/- (5p) per hour, it was an affordable and enjoyable way to race each other and Johnny, knowing that Dicky was going back to Yoxall in a few days, had suggested it.

On this particular day, they had finished their sport and were making their way back to the boat sheds when another similar boat, rowed by a kid of similar size, drew alongside Johnny's. The kid stood up, put one foot into Johnny's boat and proceeded to punch Johnny about the head and his arms put up for protection. Dicky, a few months older than Johnny, shouted at the kid, who responded with a defiant threat to 'give him one' as well. Dicky, who could see the kid was about his own age and size, readily accepted the challenge and the three boats docked.

"Up at the old farm then," the other kid said and led the way out of the park, up to the vacant farm land and house remains opposite the Public Library in School Road. On the way to the old farm, later to be a site for 'prefabs', the emergency housing for homeless and 'bombed out' families, Johnny explained that a few days previously, he had, rather unwisely, shouted some cheek at this kid, from a safe distance of course, because the kid was Jackie Kelly, a bit of a scrapper with a reputation. Not surprising with a name like that.

Dicky wasn't too bothered. He hadn't had a scrap since the one with Reggie Kettle the previous summer and this kid was no bigger than him and looked even skinnier. Dicky was sure of his own ability. He may not have had a fight recently, but he practised quite often alone on the farm, just prancing about and punching the side of the haystack or sacks of grain. Also he was fit and felt strong. The daily milking, then cleaning of the cowshed before breakfast and the one and a quarter mile walk to school, plus the manhandling of sacks of grain on Saturdays, ensured that.

The two combatants squared up, fists up at the ready. Kelly was grinning in a sort of wolfish way, he clearly enjoyed a scrap. This unsettled Dicky's composure and as he tentatively started his move forward, following the dictates of his father's instructions given to him several years before. Jackie Kelly exploded from his crouching position and a left, round arm, punch smacked into Dicky's head and right ear with a stinging force that belied the visual impression of Kelly's scrawny, bony knuckled, clenched fists. Dicky quickly stepped back. This wasn't in the plan. This kid was quick, could punch hard and was crouching ready to come in again, the same look of joyful eagerness on his thin, bony face.

'What do I do now?' was one of many thoughts now racing through Dicky's smarting head. He managed to fend off Kelly's next attack, although a swinging right fist caught him slightly, as he pranced back out of the way and squared up again, his head now clearing and recovering from that first, round arm, punch on his, still smarting, ear. Kelly was a swinger! An effective one too. The realisation was as sudden as the obvious antidote drilled into Dicky, by his father, a few years earlier. 'Go forward, punch straight, hard, fast and in this case, hope you connect', because Dicky didn't want to cop another punch like the first one.

Kelly came in again. This time Dicky, instead of stepping back and prancing around, stepped forward, at the same time punching straight ahead and slightly downwards. Bang! One, two, three and a fourth, all the punches landed square between Kelly's eyes. The change was instant and remarkable. Kelly had got both hands up to his face and was moaning, "my eyes, my eyes! I've got bad eyes! I'm s'posed to wear glasses but I 'ate 'em!"

Dicky's knuckles were a bit sore too, but he was elated and could hardly believe his good fortune.

Johnny Arnold, who had watched the activity with all the gleeful and very natural, anticipation of any kid watching any fight, had soaked someones hanky, could have been any old bit of cloth found nearby, in a puddle, and Kelly bathed his eyes and face with it.

Now grinning again, he said "there's some blood on ya' ear mate!" and offered the wet cloth, which Johnny dabbed on Dicky's ear, slightly damaged between his own skull and Kelly's bony knuckles.

Kelly continued "we gotta shake 'ands mate. Me dad told me to always shake 'ands after a fight, cos fighters make good mates."

They shook hands and parted company. Dicky would often wonder what became of Jackie Kelly.

Mill Games

Dicky had finished the milling and manoeuvred the resultant full sacks of coarse flour up to the second floor, with the help of the water-powered hoist.

Sitting on top of the last of the 20 sacks neatly stacked in rows, tied necks uppermost for ease of handling, he surveyed the scene of recent frenetic activity with some satisfaction. Apart from the steady rumbling of the, still turning water driven wheel, and the millstones grinding on themselves, there was now an air of stillness. Even the flour-laden dust was visibly clearing and settling, adding to the layers of dust built up over the centuries.

"Aye lad, built in the 1400's, or so I'm told" Uncle Bert had said one day in answer to Dicky's question. "Wheel 'as been rebuilt a time or two I reckon, as has one or two other things, no doubt. Building's the same though, so is the stream. Well, different watter I suppose."

Dicky knew, within 10 minutes or so, what the time was. Apart from the massive ornate grandfather clock which stood in the hall refusing to work properly, despite Uncle's occasional tinkering, puffing swearing and spitting, the only other clock, anywhere on the farm, was the traditional kitchen wall clock. Uncle corrected it each day by the Greenwich meantime signal, broadcast immediately before the first morning news of the day on the BBC. Uncle Bert kept a large silver watch in his waistcoat pocket. It was attached to a chain, the other end of which was secured through a buttonhole in his waistcoat. He would make a great play of taking the watch out occasionally, looking at it for some time, then remarking "I can safely say, as near as dammit, that it's thereabouts, either to, or past." He'd then chuckle and say, for the benefit of any newcomer, "nowt ever works proper on or near me lad, so dunna stand too close."

Farmers, by the very nature of their work, just knew, within a minute or two, how long each daily chore took and Dicky now had a good idea too. He reckoned that he'd got at least 15 minutes to put into action the plan he'd been working on in his head for several weeks.

Auntie would be preparing the thick sandwiches for lunch filled with corned beef or cheese. Uncle would still be hedging and could be seen from the middle floor of the mill, where Dicky was sitting. He slid down off the sack, went across the floor to the loading door, which he unbolted and opened. Across the road and at the far end of the first field, he could make out the figure of Uncle Bert, reaching, cutting and gathering. "Yep!" Dicky said to himself, "another five minutes cutting and ten minutes to walk back."

Excitement already welling up inside, Dicky shut and bolted the door, scurried across the mill floor to the trap door and fed the steel chain of the hoist down through the 3 inch hole at the centre of two split doors. He then scampered down the single flight of wooden steps to the bottom floor, stepped across to the lowered chain and pulled through sufficient to attach to the neck of a sack of unmilled grain. Quickly, expertly and with the help of the hoist, he dragged the sack into position directly below the split doors. He then sat on top of the sack, his hands gripping the chain secured to the sack neck, with his legs either side. Comfortable and secure, he looked up at the split doors about 3 feet above his head. His intention was to ride on top of the sack upwards through those doors which, when struck by a rising sack, swung open, bounced back against the sides of the emerging sack and finally fell back into their original place after the sack had passed through. The upward progress of anything on the chain could be controlled at each of the 3 levels of the mill by a pull on the hoist rope, which hung alongside the chain and which Dicky would have hold of. When the sack, with Dicky aboard, cleared the split doors, he would give another tug on the rope, the upward progress would stop and the weight of the sack and Dicky would gently return them to the new floor level. Dicky would then get off, return things to normal and start working on his telling of his 'new' game to his pal Bob, next time he saw him.

Dicky's only problem, or so he thought, was how to get through the doors without banging his head into them. Grinning in the sure knowledge that he had already worked out the solution, Dicky clambered down, cut a length of binding twine, carefully folded lengthwise an empty hession sack he'd put ready and climbed back on top of the full one.

He then wrapped the folded sack around the chain about 6 inches above his head and secured it with the twine, the resultant lump being much larger than the hole in the split doors, but much smaller than a full sack. Trying to control his eagerness, Dicky thought the whole thing through again. He was satisfied. All was ready.

Dusty the cat, patiently sitting motionless, its eyes focused on a point under the chute behind the flour collecting box, hadn't moved a muscle while all these preparations were going on. Dicky had realised some time ago why the bluish grey tomcat had got its name. The descending flour dust had altered its appearance from sleek and shiny to almost a dull stone colour, quite still and apparently lifeless, apart from its eyes which glowed with a baleful intensity, waiting....

This was it. His heart pounding with excitement, Dicky gripped the chain below the lump of sacking with his left hand. With his right hand, he pulled down on the hoist rope and, with a jerk, immediately started to ascend, seemingly much faster than he anticipated. Perhaps it was the sudden upward jerk which slightly unsettled him. Whatever, Dicky certainly didn't feel in control when the first trapdoors crashed open and bounced back against his emerging head and shoulders. The almost simultaneous blows disorientated him and caused his left leg to relax from its grip on the sack of grain and catch on something on its passage through, causing Dicky to spin whilst still going up. Now he was swaying, swinging and frantically trying to grasp the hoist clutch rope he'd unintentionally let go of. BANG! The sacking hit the second set of trap doors with exactly the same result as before. More punishment for Dicky's head and shoulders. Then, miraculously, everything stopped.

In a daze, Dicky pulled his legs upwards through the trap doors, just about fell off the sack and ended up lying, backside down, in the open-top grain hopper, the steep, polished, sloping sides of which, threatened to swallow him whole. Dazed and feebly struggling to get some sort of grip on the smooth sides, his battered mind vaguely registered that the wheel and stones were slowing down and the juddering and shaking was ceasing, as was the sound of rushing and splashing water. Someone must have closed off the millwheel sluice gate! And that someone was now shouting and clattering up the wooden stairs.

"My God!! What in tarnation youm bin a'doin?"

Uncle Bert, red-faced from his exertions and stooping in the confined space adjacent to the feed hopper, struggled to get his breath as his eyes got used to the dimness and began a cursory examination of the scene.

"Are y' hurt lad? I mean hurt bad like. Can you move y' arms n'legs? I canna see any blood, well not yet anyways."

He said no more and gently lifted Dicky out of the hopper and helped him down to the bottom floor.

"Well, their inna nowt broke lad" he said as he sat Dicky down on the stone steps outside the mill. He continued "but you maun hurt some, I've never sin y' so still, aye."

He sat next to Dicky, rummaged through his pockets for his pipe and 'baccy', got a good 'un going, spit a couple of times, leaned back against the mill wall and said "well? Are y' gonna tell me or 'ave I got to work it out mesen?"

Dicky was hurt. He felt sore and tender just about everywhere on his body and his head felt as if it should be pouring with blood. Scratches and abrasions were plentiful and bruising and swelling were already appearing. What hurt Dicky also was the fact that he had failed. His carefully worked out plan had gone wrong and nearly catastrophically so, if Uncle hadn't arrived on the scene timely enough to halt things!

Painfully, through the tears, Dicky explained. Uncle sat and listened. He didn't even spit and his pipe, untended, went out.

"By 'eck!" he murmured a couple of times, "by 'eck!"

After a while he said "c'mon, lets get summat to eat afore Auntie feeds it to Sammy."

They wandered across the farmyard and up the path to the farmhouse. If they had looked back, they would have seen Dusty settling down on the stone step their backsides had just warmed up, his belly full and sleepy.

Auntie listened quietly, busying herself making the mugs of hot Bovril and serving the sandwiches, as Uncle narrated the events in the mill. Apart from the occasional clicking of her false teeth and the pursing of her lips, she showed little interest until he'd finished.

Then she snorted, "Inna you got no sense at all? Are y' gunna grow up as daft as this big lummox 'ere then!"

Uncle bridled at that, "I inna that daft Auntie!" he said.

"I inna your Auntie, y' big fool. I'm your wife!"

"Aye lass, and the best pasty maker and wife on this farm, inna no doubt about it" he chuckled.

"As the only woman on the farm, that canna be difficult," Auntie snorted back.

"Well, I'll grant y' that y' the only two legged female beast here, but youm still the best" Uncle, very bravely, countered.

Auntie paused for a moment, then reached for the long handled warming pan that hung by the kitchen range. Adopting an aggressive stance and gritting her ill-fitting teeth, she whispered in a menacing low voice "Herbert Roe, if I hear as much as one more word from y', then I swear to God I'll fetch this pan across y' daft head."

Uncle leaned back, smiled contentedly and said nothing. He was already getting some personal satisfaction from the reactions he was sure to get from the telling and retelling of Dicky's escapade.

In the next few days Dicky would be amazed at the subtle exaggerations Uncle would make to the saga, for that is what it had become, and wondered how many more tellings there would be before he, Dicky, finished up on the roof of the mill, alongside the sack of grain and possibly the hoist round his neck. His plan may have failed, but Uncle Bert made it sound like glorious failure, easily outlasting the misery and pain.

Billy Bacon

With the pain forgotten and only a few yellowing bruises remaining, only Dicky's damaged ego reminded him of the previous week's plan failure at the mill. There was no milling to be done this Saturday and Dicky was sitting on the mill stone step carving a pattern in the green bark of a straight piece of branch he'd cut from the many hedges around. Nellie was lying near his feet taking advantage of the warm autumn sun. Suddenly her ears pricked up and her now raised head, followed immediately be a scattering of dried corn husks, straw and dirt, as she energetically struggled to her feet.

Even before the little car had turned into the farm drive and into view, Nellie was barking like crazy. Her almost immediate, visual confirmation, then caused her to, still barking, start jumping around in circles, doing a fair imitation of an animated, stiff legged rocking horse. Dicky watched as the car wended its way through the holes and furrows worn by the passage of cows and the occasional horse and cart over the last century and more. It drove right up into the farmyard, turned right and parked inside the open fronted corrugated steel barn where the old, now unused, farm equipment was kept. Like other dirt grubbing, forever hard up, small farmers up and down the land, Bert Roe just could not throw anything away. "Eh lad! Nowt wuss than findin' y'need summat youm jus'got rid of."

The car door opened and the scrawniest little bloke Dicky had ever seen stepped, or rather stumbled out, as Nellie was jumping all over him in excitement.

"Orlright! Orlright! Crikey! Yer wuss than ever. For cryin' out loud, just wait a minnit, will ya?"

Scrawny leaned back into the car and fetched out a small newspaper wrapped parcel, which he held above his head. Nellie was now going frantic and making the most torturous racket, with her backside on the ground and her head right back, eyes closed and mouth wide open. Scrawny grinned, took the proffered paw and shook it.

"That's a good gal. That's my gal. Now say please. Go on now, please!"

Nellie closed and opened her mouth several times, the anticipatory drooling flying all over the place, then lay down and rolled over on her back, her furiously wagging tail flinging dislodged dried cow muck, straw, chaff and grit from between the yard cobbles which had probably housed them for months.

Still holding the parcel high above his head, Scrawny carefully unwrapped it and, just as carefully, revealed the contents, a large bone, the remains of a shoulder of ham. Nellie was now in a controlled state of near madness. She obviously desperately wanted to leap up and grab her idea of paradise, but was experienced enough to know that she had to continue with this, pointless to her, charade. Lying 'doggo', apart from uncontrollable tail and whimpering, lip-licking, eyes bulging, disinterest? You wouldn't bet!

"That's my gal! Come on then!" Before the words were out of Scrawny's mouth, Nellie had displaced half a sackful of debris from the cobbles in her frenetic effort to right herself and get into the obligatory 'dog begging' position again, mouth wide open, eyes full of pleading. "Good gal!"

Scrawny lowered his hand and presented the bone to Nellie. She tentatively sniffed it, just once, then with a "Grumph!" snatched it from Scrawny's grasp, wheeled round and triumphantly sped round the corner behind the barn.

"Gone to bury it!" Scrawny exclaimed and laughed. "She don't get any better behaved. I'm the only one who can tease 'er like that. She'd bite any other buggar's 'and off fust."

"Aye! That's right enough." Uncle Bert had made his way round from the orchard where he had been preparing for his friend's visit for the weekend. "This 'ere is Billy Bacon, an old friend. 'e lives in Burton an' drives a bus. I feeds 'im an 'e 'elps me. 'inna much wrong wi' that, is there now!"

They shook hands and made their way up the garden path to the farmhouse where Auntie had the mugs of tea all ready and waiting.

She fussed around Billy like a mother hen. "A currant pasty Bill?"

"Yes please!"

"Another drop o' tea Bill?"

"Yes please!"

"Y' dunna get any fatter! An' y' eat like an' 'oss!" Billy Bacon grinned,

"It's 'cos I'm allus on the move Tilly."

"Aye!" responded Auntie, somewhat resignedly.

They finished their tea and as planned, made their way to the adjacent orchard. Both Uncle Bert and Uncle Bill, as Auntie had suggested Dicky call him, reckoned they could finish picking the apples before the 4.30 milking. Auntie, Dicky and Uncle Bert had picked all the apples at the lower level. It was just the higher branches that were the annual difficulty, unlike the modern orchards of uniform medium height. Uncle Bert manoeuvred the sectional wooden ladder into various positions, whereupon Billy would, almost like a circus performer, climb up, two rungs at a time, reaching out at all angles, grabbing apples, sometimes with both hands, and dropping them to Dicky and Auntie waiting with outstretched blanket held off the ground. Within about 3 hours, all the apples were accounted for, except for the couple of branches at the top of the highest tree, which was considerably higher than the top of the chimneys of the farmhouse.

"Right Bill! What sort of stunt are y'gunna pull this year then?" Uncle Bert asked as he got a firm grip on the ladder. "Are y' gunna swing off the top branch like you did last year?"

"No I ain't!" responded Billy. "I'm getting' too old for this caper an' I don't bounce as well anymore."

He steadily climbed the ladder until, aided by gripping surrounding branches, he could stand on the very top rung and pull the fruit laden branches towards him, whereupon he picked and dropped the fruit to the waiting catchers below. On completion of his particular task, he started to make his way down. But not for long.

He appeared to be stuck and could be heard muttering curses. "What in tarnation are y'doin'?" shouted Uncle Bert.

"I've got some of the ladder up inside me trouser leg," shouted Billy. More curses followed and Dicky moved away from the ladder to try and get a better view of Billy, partly obscured by the foliage beneath him. From his new vantage point, Dicky could see Billy's left foot two rungs below his right foot, which was on the top rung of the ladder and the outline of the end of the ladder side-piece threatening to break out from the inside of Billy's trousers. The unfortunate Billy was hanging on to a couple of branches obviously not strong enough for him to pull himself back up again and his struggles to do so had caused his body weight to take over.

"I'm just 'aving a breather" Billy called down, now panting worse than Nellie.

Uncle Bert, who couldn't see as clearly as Dicky, called up. "What d'you want us to do?"

"Nowt! Bert. I'll manage."

Uncle Bert looked worried and when Dicky described Billy's predicament, looked even more worried. He again called up "If I send Dicky up, can 'e do owt?"

"No," came back the strangulated reply. "If I fall, I'll bring 'im down as well."

"Strewth!" Uncle muttered. He motioned to Auntie, who was standing there all agitated, chewing on nothing, her hands wringing her pinafore.

"Come over 'ere Tilly, an' you lad!" He got on the bottom rung of the ladder and said, "I'm a'gooin up. You lad, get on the ladder be'ind me and stand still on the second or third rung. Auntie. You stand on the bottom rung an' both keep still." He started to climb the ladder very steadily and called up, "just another minit Billy. I'm on my way."

Billy's response was a weak rasping "careful Bert!"

Uncle Bert was steadily climbing as carefully as possible, but with his greater bulk and weight was having some difficulty negotiating the branches, not being agile and speedy like Billy. As he climbed through the middle section of the fully extended ladder, one arm mostly engaged holding aside branches, the greater flexibility caused the ladder to shake almost uncontrollably and Uncle had to stop for a few seconds, after each step. Dicky knew it was serious, because Auntie had stopped chewing her gums and remained silent. There was no sound from Billy and the only sound was Uncle's puffing and the movement of foliage, now completely hiding him.

Then, after what seemed like ages, Uncle Bert's voice filtered through. "Right Bill! I'm tekkin' y'weight on me showders. Y'weigh nowt, so it's no problem."

Another couple of minutes went by, then thankfully, Bill's voice, "I'll be OK now. If you can just push me up enough for me to get hold of a bigger branch, I can sort meself out."

There were a few more minutes of puffing and muttering then Uncle Bert called down, "We'm orlright an' we'm acomin' down!"

Dicky looked round at Auntie's face just below his. She'd started chewing her gums again, her upturned face and gaze directed on the branches where the ladder disappeared from view. The vibrating ladder and puffing preceded the first sight of Uncle Bert's legs, then body, steadily descending, closely followed by Billy. The first to speak, when they both reached the ground, was Auntie.

"I'll get some tea on!" she said and marched off, cheeks now flaming red. The words "Daftest pair of grown up kids I've ever sin!" floated back, as still muttering and flailing the air with the 'pinny' she had pulled off in her agitation, she stamped out of the orchard and into the kitchen.

"I'm gonna cop it now!" Billy said with a weak grin.

"Aye, but you'll be agooin yom tomorrer, an' I'll be coppin' it for at least a wik!" replied Uncle.

Dicky grinned and said nothing. Everything was back to normal and the immediate future was suddenly very promising. Uncle Billy wasn't going home until tomorrow! Great!

"Ever bin Ferrettin'?"

Apart from the 5pm milking, Sunday's work was done and breakfast eaten by 10am.

Dicky had been up and down like a scalded cat, running here and there on Uncle Billy's instructions. He knew that something was afoot, because of the items Billy said they'd need. Half a dozen hession sacks, at least a dozen sharpened small stakes, a roll of binding twine, a sackful of old newspaper with some lamp oil dripped on here and there, a small spade and a hammer.

In about 10 minutes flat, Dicky had got the lot and was ready to go. Uncle Bert and Billy, none the worse for yesterday's antics, apart from a 'stretch mark' in the bottom of his old bus uniform, right trouser leg, came down the garden path to where Dicky was sitting on the pile of sacks.

Uncle Billy walked right past Dicky to the barn where his little motor was, Uncle Bert following, picking up and carrying the sacks and stakes. Dicky quickly gathered up the rest of the items and scurried after them, frightened to death in case he missed something.

What was going on? Billy opened the car door and lifted out, what appeared to be, a wooden box, about 15" square, with a handle on top. One side consisted of a hinged framed steel mesh, shut and secured with a steel hook and eye. Through the mesh could be seen, what looked like a white, very long, rat, moving from corner to corner and stretching upwards to examine the upper corners too.

"Jeepers! What's that?" yelped Dicky, dropping his burden and pushing his face close up to get a good look.

"Don't get to close Dicky lad!" Billy said quietly. "That mean looking fellah is a very 'ungry ferret, 'an if'n you get to close, e'll 'ave your nose for breakfast. Ain't y'ever bin ferrettin'?"

Dicky had heard about ferrets and ferreting for rabbits, but this was the first time that he'd seen one up close and, he, Dicky was going to be involved in ferreting. He was excited. More so, because by now, he'd already realised that the presence of Billy Bacon guaranteed enthusiasm, chance, risk-taking and good humour, whatever the situation. Even when having a nap after a meal, he looked like a little relaxed jumping jack firework, liable to go off at any second. You just never knew with Billy Bacon.

"When was 'e last fed then?" Uncle Bert asked.

"Dunno! I ain't fed 'im since I collected 'im Friday night, so 'e must be bloody starving" replied Billy.

"Well I inna gunna touch n' then, an' that's for sure" said Uncle. "Youm in charge o' that thing!"

Billy grinned, lifted up the box head high by the handle and said to the ferret, "come on Nipper! Let's go a'ferrettin'."

They trooped off, Uncle Bert leading the way across the first field, over the bridge and to the far side of the second field, where the rabbit warren was, and out of hearing of the continuous mournful racket made by Nellie, unfairly barred on this expedition.

"Dog is too daft for rabbitting!" said Billy. "She can't keep quiet an' she can't keep still!"

"Bit like you then!" said Uncle. "An' youm 'ere!"

"Aye! an' so is Nipper, an' only I knows 'ow to 'andle 'im. If it worn't f'me, where would you be" countered Billy.

"At church with Tilly, like as not, like most other Sundays," said Uncle Bert, who continued, "youm a bad influence on us Billy Bacon!"

Bert and Billy grinned at each other, secure in their friendship and trusting of each other. Dicky loved it.

Billy went from hole to hole examining the ground closely. "Looking for fresh droppings!" he said, in answer to Dicky's query.

The freshest droppings apparently indicated the hole the rabbit had last gone down. After a few minutes Billy was satisfied. "This'll do. We'll put the ferret down this 'ole, but let's block off the others fust."

Dicky watched as Billy placed the open end of the sack round one of the holes and secured it with four stakes, which he banged in with the hammer. He passed the hammer to Dicky saying, "if y'want some fun, y'got t'do a bit o'work fust. 'Ave a go at some of them other 'oles!"

Dicky eagerly complied and whilst the others had a smoke, soon had three other holes covered. The remaining four or five holes, apart from the one selected by Billy, were blocked off by the simple expedient of chopping into the roof of the entrances with the spade, or filling the entrance with a rolled up sack.

"Right! This is the plan," said Billy. "Bert 'ere, will tie the end of this string." He pulled out of his pocket a ball of white string and passed it to Uncle, "to the ring on Nipper's collar."

Billy put his right hand into a leather 'hedging' glove, opened the mesh door of the wooden box with his left hand, reached in and lifted out the ferret, which, seemingly quite docile, nestled down in the crook of Billy's arm.

"I inna gunna put my 'ands anywhere that thing" said Uncle, and why d'y call it Nipper? It looks a bit mean to me."

The ferret had got it nose in the air, trying to detect some scent of food, no doubt.

"An' why, if it's so friendly, as y'got that 'edgin' glove on?"

Billy, feeling very comfortable about Uncle Bert's discomfort said, "look, 'e only likes young, fresh killed, meat. 'e ain't gonna be interested in your tough old carcass!" He went on, "you can stroke 'im if you like", but seeing Dicky move forward said, "Not you lad, you're too young an' fresh."

Uncle Bert studiously gazed at Nipper for a couple of minutes, stuck his pipe, which had now gone out, in his pocket, grabbed the string and moved closer, extending his large, callused hands, towards Nipper. The ferret didn't seem too bothered at all. The only thing noticeable to Dicky, was its eyes, which didn't appear to be interested in Uncle Bert's hands, but his face. Nipper was actually staring Uncle Bert down, or appeared to be trying to.

"Watch 'is ears!" said Billy quietly. "If y'see 'is ears go back, y'knows 'es about to strike! Then it's all about oo's quickest." Billy chuckled. He was really enjoying his friend's unease.

Uncle Bert was quite still, his hands now stationary. He could cope with large farm animals, probably even bulls, but he'd got a good working knowledge of them. This was a bit different. Nipper looked like a big rat and he hated and detested rats, the sole reason he'd got two cats at the farm. The cats were never fed. They hunted and ate rats and mice, both being a plague to his animal feed and grain for milling. They were not cuddly cats, to be stroked and fussed. In fact they looked quite mean, especially Dusty. They were never hungry for long.

"I canna see if 'is ears is back'ds or forrods" said Uncle, also a bit quiet-like. "I knows I dunna care for the way it's lookin' at me!"

"Oh! gi' us the string!" said a now exasperated Billy. "We'll be 'ere all day, if we waits for you."

He took the string and tied it through the ring on Nipper's collar, all the time Nipper sniffing his fingers, but at no time even looking like wanting to bite.

"Right Dicky!" said Billy, getting up and walking towards the open hole, carrying Nipper, who was now getting a bit agitated. "You are the quickest, so you'll have to look after two holes. The two nearest to each other. When I puts Nipper down this 'ole, 'e'll be down after 'is dinner damn quick! So you'll 'ave to be ready, cos the rabbits don't want to be anyone's dinner either."

He paused, looked at Uncle Bert with a grin and continued. "Bert 'ere is gettin' too fat and slow for this game, so I'm depending on you."

"Pity I dinna move a bit quicker yesterday an' left you up the bloody apple tree!" countered Uncle with a chuckle, knowing he'd scored with that one.

Billy bravely tried to shrug it off and said, "I'd a bin allright! I was just resting a bit up there!"

"Oh yeh!" countered Uncle. "If youm 'ad a rested much longer, your little bullet 'ead would've med an 'ole in the ground an' we wunna be buggerin' about 'ere!"

Uncle Bert knew he'd got the better of that exchange, but he also knew that it wouldn't be for long, so he whistled and hummed as he got into position near the hole furthest away from Nipper's entrance.

"What do I do when a rabbit runs into a sack?" enquired Dicky, realising that, with the exchange of banter between the two old friends, Billy had forgotten to continue with his instructions.

"Aye lad! Right! What the pair on y'do, an' this I got to see," said Billy, giving Uncle a wicked sidelong, smirking, glance, "is to get a foot on the sack, between the rabbit an' the 'ole e's just come out 'n. Then, pull out the stakes an' twist the top o' the sack into a knot."

Billy paused for breath and continued. "Then put the sack an' rabbit into the 'ole entrance so no other rabbit can get out that way."

Billy grinned, bent down with his face near the hole and shouted, "'ere comes a playmate for yer!"

He placed the, now very, eager Nipper down, in the entrance of the hole and with no hesitation, Nipper disappeared, the string dragging quickly behind him. Billy, jumping up and down like a man possessed, was doling out the string and excitedly yelling, "look at 'im go! 'E must a gone thirty feet or more an' still shiftin'! Wi' a bit o' luck, we'll 'ave three or four of the perishin' rabbits within minnits!"

He let out about another ten feet of slack, secured his end of the string by tying it to the spade, then took up position at the remaining sack covered hole. "Won't be long now!" he said, all tensed and ready to pounce. The scene would remain with Dicky for the rest of his life.

The three North American Indian hunters, having set their traps, now waited, silent, motionless and downwind from their quarry, a magnificent young Bison bull. The beast, occasionally lifting it's head to sniff the light breeze, moved slowly towards the waiting trap, which when sprung would provide meat, leather and horn for the squaws of their tribe, to prepare and store for the harder winter times ahead. Time seemed to stand still, nothing new for the patient hunters, the light breeze occasionally stirring the long strands of their straight black hair across the nut brown skin of their temples and necks. They waited, poised in the shelter of their cover, strategically placed and ready to shoot their lethal arrows, from three different angles, into the vital organs of the beast.

A few more minutes passed and one of the hunters moved and broke the silence. "I'm a'getting' cramp an' I think weem a'wastin' our time!" said Uncle Bert, somewhat miserably, as it now looked, more than likely, that there would be no rabbit to put with the vegetables and pastry Auntie would, at this moment, be preparing.

"I dunno what 'as gone wrong!" said Billy, equally gloomy. "Nipper must a' disturbed summat by now."

Dicky didn't know what to say, so said nothing. The two men lit up and smoked for a few minutes whilst their gaze wandered from the, now unmoving, string to the various holes and back again.

"String ain't moved for ages!" Billy said mournfully."

"Maybe Nipper is stuck!" volunteered Dicky.

At that, Billy stepped on the discarded remains of his cigarette and said, "well! ere' goes!" He picked up the spade, untied the string which he passed to Dicky and said, "ere lad, 'ang on to this. I've got t'do some diggin'. If Nipper stars movin' agin', tell us!"

With that Billy started to dig a trench above the route indicated by the string, which went deeper at a downward angle. As Billy dug out the red sandy soil, it became obvious that a long day's digging lay ahead. Both men took turns digging, following the string, which Billy gave a little tug on, now and again, with no response.

"I don't understand any o' this!" grunted Billy plaintively. "If I don't get Nipper back, I'm gonna be in right muck an' no mistek!"

About an hour had passed of steady digging, following the string along what appeared to be the main tunnel, criss-crossed occasionally by other tunnels. Also revealed was one larger area, in which was some dried grass.

"That be a nest for the young!" said Billy, his feet a good 4ft below the surface. "There must a bin a fair few o'the blighters! Where in 'ell's name are they? an' look. The damn string's movin' agin!"

Dicky was standing in the trench, idly looking around, when some movement caught his eye. He looked across to the hedge, where something again sort of flashed and was gone. He climbed out of the diggings, ran across to the hedge, peering in and through the dense foliage, trying to seek out a gap. Suddenly, he yelled. He'd found a bigger gap and could see through at what had caught his eye.

"It's Nipper! An' e's all red!"

"You'd be red if y'd bin crawlin' through that soil!" grunted Billy, as he scrambled out of the trench and made his way across the top of the rabbit warren. Even Uncle Bert, who had been lying on his back with his hands behind his head, had moved and was lumbering across to where Billy was looking through a clearing in the hedge.

"Well I'll be a Rhubarb tree!" said Uncle Bert. "Just look at all them 'oles!"

It was immediately obvious that rabbits completely ignore hedges when they decide to build warrens, for most of this particular warren was the other side of the hedge, in a field not belonging to Uncle.

"We can get through down at the stream's edge," said Uncle, already on his way, Billy and Dicky close behind.

It was only 40 yards or so and they didn't even get their feet wet, the stream being fairly low after a dry spell. As they approached Nipper, who seemed interested only in sitting up and licking his furry chest, Billy realised what the colour was.

"Blimey! It's ruddy blood! An' look at 'is tummy. It's fit t'bust! 'e musta bin starvin'!"

Dicky was amazed at Nipper's appearance. He seemed twice as big and looked as if someone had dipped him headfirst into a pot of pink paint.

Billy untied the string from Nipper's collar so that Dicky could pull it back through the warren and Nipper nestled down in the crook of Billy's arm and closed his eyes. He looked very contented. More than you could say for Billy and Uncle as they wended their way back, not very hurriedly, to gather up and collect their gear.

"I wonder 'ow many rabbits come flyin' out of them 'oles!" said Billy.

"All of 'em!, except the bloody slowest!" replied Uncle. He continued, "They were probably watchin' us dig an' laffin' themsels stupid!"

"What are we gonna say to Tilly?" asked Billy.

"Gawd only knows," replied Uncle Bert. "She'll be fating mad when she 'ears about this. We better get Dicky to tell 'er fust! Gie 'er chance t'calm down afore we gets theer."

Uncle Bert took the stuff Dicky was carrying and said "Goo on Dicky! Run on ahead an' tell Auntie we inna got a rabbit, but weem got a big fat ferret she can put in the pie!"

Later on that day, they all had vegetable pie with vegetables and a weak, OXO flavoured gravy. No one complained!

Billy of course, couldn't keep his mouth shut for long. "Nice pastry Tilly! Nice pastry."

Auntie pursed her lips and straightened her back. She glared at them through her wire rimmed thick lens spectacles for a few seconds, relaxed, smiled and began to chuckle. "Three on yer! 'alf a day's work, me 'ere preparin' the pastry an'such," she paused, "an' 'oo gets the rabbit? The blasted ferret!"

They all burst out laughing and Billy nipped up to the outdoor in his car and fetched a quart of beer and a bottle of 'pop'.

About an hour later, Dicky just had to voice his concern about something that had been bothering him. "Why did you ask me to put all that oily newspaper in the bag and take with us?"

Billy looked at Uncle Bert, and then they both looked at Auntie, whose pursed lips and raised eyebrows were asking the same question.

"Well?" Auntie said.

After some hesitation, Billy replied "We don't want to talk about it," and both men relaxed, chuckling.

"You wunna get any sense out of them now they've got some ale in their bellies." Auntie said resignedly.

"Pick y' Stick an' Stop y' Blitherin'!"

School holidays at Yoxall were timed to coincide with the annual maincrop potato harvest in September/October. Children, minimum age 12 years, had the choice of organised potato picking on a fulltime basis for 4 weeks, for which they received 29 shillings (£1.45p) weekly, or help around their own home or school gardens for nowt! This arrangement lasted for the full holiday term of 4 weeks. Naturally, most kids, some reluctantly, went 'tater pickin', the generous payment, same for all ages, being a massive supplement to family incomes. In Dicky's case it would be a massive boost to his savings and his dream of buying a racing bike.

The 20 or so Yoxall kids, including Dicky, Bob Mewis and Pete Sharrat, would be picked up at 8am and transported, on a flat trailer towed by a tractor, to the potato growing farm in Kings Bromley, about 3 miles away. Once there, they would resume the previous positions they had left the previous working day at 'their stick', a measured length of the rows of potatoes to be harvested, 2 or 3 rows each time the tractor drawn 'flail' came round, lifting and throwing them out, where they would lay on the surface of the ground until they were collected.

At the start of work on any one of the large fields to be harvested, one of the men, usually the farmer, would pace out and mark with a stick pushed into the soft soil, lengths of about 20 paces. Once the 'pickers', some times 50 or more depending on the size of the field, had positioned themselves on both sides of the field at each stick, the waiting tractor driver, having already disconnected the trailer and 'hitched up' the 'tater flail', would commence to traverse the field, up one side and down the other, 'lifting' 2 or 3 rows each time he passed.

Each 'picker', carrying a small round wicker basket, would leap into action as soon as the 'flail' passed by leaving in its wake, the contents, stones, roots and potatoes, of the rows it had just lifted and thrown sideways. Once the small basket was filled, it was carried and emptied into a larger basket which, when full, was emptied into a high sided trailer by another tractor driver, whose responsibility was to empty and return the large baskets to within a few feet of the pickers and convey the picked potatoes to large open earth clamps, where they would be covered with straw and soil to protect them from the ravages of winter.

Very few fields were square, resulting in 'end of row' pickers having more, or less, to pick, depending on the angle of the hedge at the end of the rows. To compensate this, the farmer, or very often, the pickers themselves, would move the sticks accordingly, but sometimes, in the absence of the farmer or any willingness of the next 'picker' in line to co-operate, some friction would develop.

On one occasion, Dicky, who had 'copped' for the last stick in a field of angled edges, moved his stick a couple of paces to reduce his rapidly growing 'stick length'. His neighbouring picker, a woman, probably a mother, was equally determined not to increase her 'stick' or move her stick, even a little. She yelled at Dicky "pick y' stick an' stop y' blitherin', youm' a lot younger an' faster than we'em."

Dicky, somewhat mortified, could see her point and carried on picking as fast as he could. Eventually the tractor driver reached the end of the field and had to stop whilst Dicky scrambled all over the ground feverishly picking the last yard or so. Understanding the situation immediately, the driver, himself a bit 'brassed off' for having to stop, tried to salvage the dispute by adjusting several of the sticks, but the woman wasn't having any of that.

"I inna pickin' any more than the length I started wi', an' that's that" she said, grimly gripping the stick and refusing to let go.

The driver hesitated only for a moment. "Right" he said and turned and made his way back over the rows of undug potatoes towards the field gate, the other side of which could be seen the farmers car.

"Now you'm forrit," said one of the several women making up the labour force. "Miserable owd sod inna gunna be 'appy 'bout no one a'workin'."

The first woman, still gripping her stick, said nothing, but the determined set of her face was sufficient proof that she would not be easily persuaded.

The man soon reappeared, accompanied by the farmer complete with his particular badge of office, an old, wide brimmed trilby type hat that had seen better days. His long raincoat, which could have, once upon a time, belonged to a railways ticket collector, had capacious pockets which easily accommodated essentials, wire, twine, pliers, tobacco, pipe, matches, small notebook, pencil and penknife. The legs of his corduroy work trousers complete with their long service 'medals', patches, stitches, new tears and worn holes, ended about 2" above the tops of his standard hobnailed boots and about 6" above ground level. In particularly cold weather, he would top the lot with an old RAF aircrew fleece lined jacket, he had probably scrounged from RAF personnel at nearby Fradley airfield, maybe even won it playing airmen at darts in one of the local pubs.

The farmer didn't hesitate. Grim-faced, and starting at the top of the field, he went along the rows re-pacing an extra pace for each 'stick' and then moving and replacing the sticks. Nobody moved or resisted until he came to the main contender, her hand still firmly gripping the stick. The farmer stopped, looked her in the face and said "y'can bugger off now wi' pay up to this minnit," he paused, then continued, "or y'can be smart an' pick the extra pace you'm all 'as to do. They'm all 'appy 'bout it an' you'm better be. What's it gunna be?"

The woman looked around at all the pickers who had congregated to watch the action. Any allies she may have had were not showing it. She hesitated only a couple of seconds. "An extra pace 'inna so bad" she said and gave up the stick to the farmer who promptly moved it the several paces needed to complete the re-subdivision of field length.

The farmer had got out his notebook and pencil and looking at his watch said, "now get back to what youm all being well paid for and think on. Youm all workin' this field an extra 15 minutes t'day to mek up the time youm lost." He paused, and then added "any more nonsense like this an' youm all sacked. I got more important things t'sort than your silly differences."

He stomped off back to his car where he could continue his lunch of sandwiches and cold tea, not much change there.

Working farmers had been living frugally for many years and would continue to do so. The other man restarted the tractor, work recommenced and they all worked the extra 15 minutes. There were no more problems and they all kept their jobs.

It all seemed very sensible to Dicky, who would not earn such a high weekly rate until he was a 17 year old engineering apprentice, over 4 years later.

Out of his 'tater pickin' earnings during that 4 weeks, Dicky paid for brand new, all leather, hobnail boots for Duggie and himself, both at 12/6d a pair (62p). With half round steel tips on the toe and heel, and the soles covered with regimental rows of 1/8th" high steel hobnails, the boots were an exact copy of the sturdy full size boots that all agricultural workers wore and objects of pride for all boys, most of whom were destined to be farm workers anyway. The rest of the money went into his Post Office savings account and recorded in the account book, on which Dicky had written just two words, 'RACING BIKE'.

Jack the Tramp

Winter in the agricultural countryside was bleak, cold, hard and completely at the mercy of the elements. Snow ploughs were unheard of and show clearing was left to farmers with their 'cobbled up' makeshift angled metal sheets fixed to trator fronts. The nights were long and many families would spend the long evenings making things, such as pegged rugs, and repairing all sorts of odds and ends like clothes and furniture.

Dicky wondered how the local tramp managed, when he wasn't helping out at the dairy farm next door. It was owned and run by the Upton sisters and their only regular help was Jack, who lived in a makeshift den in the corner of one of their fields, all year round. In particularly severe weather, he would sometimes bed down in one of the barns. It's quite likely the Upton sisters would have allowed him in a part of the house, if he had been more presentable, but his only clothes, which he probably slept in, were always covered by a very large army greatcoat and he probably smelt somewhat worse than the animals he helped with.

He rarely spoke; in fact many people thought he was mute, but Pete Sharratt knew different. For a bit of pocket money, Pete used to help with odd jobs about the farm, which was opposite his home.

One day, whilst Pete was helping Jack to get the large herd of dairy cows in for milking, one of the Upton sisters passed by.

"Eh! I wunna mind ge'ing 'er a corve"(calf), Jack had said, very much to the amazement of Pete, who later related the story to any kid who would listen. He, most likely, would like to have told his parents what Jack had said, but also most likely, he would probably have got a good 'thraping' (hiding) for being so blasphemous. There were many Chapel folk in and around Woodmill, the rest being Church. There were very few who didn't attend one or the other each and every Sunday.

Dicky, whose parents only went to church for weddings and funerals, had only experienced Church through school and with the 'cubs', the Scout movement juniors in Yardley Wood, Birmingham. However, he was obliged to accompany Mr and Mrs Roe to St Peter's

Church in Yoxall every Sunday, for the mid morning service, a good walk each way.

"It's only a mile an a 'quatter' woman. Stop you're blitherin'," Uncle would say in response to Auntie's complaining.

"It's alright for you, y' great lummox! You inna left the dinner a'cooking. I said the vicar was gooin' on a bit. It' alright for 'im to keep askin' us to pray for this and pray for that in these tryin' times and to try and think well of them wicked German soldiers and airmen who bomb our towns and factories and frighten my poor chickens so's they stop alayin!" She paused for a breath and continued "But all I could think about for the last 10 minutes in there, was dinner and would it survive."

"Ah, goo on wi' y'. It'll be all right, it allus is. Youm too bloody crafty an' you knows it. It'll tek more than a vicar wi' a lot to say to upset your applecart."

He chuckled, stepped up the pace a bit and shouted "lef' ri' lef' ri' c, mon, pick 'em up."

Some Sundays they would all go around to Uncle Bert's sister's place for tea. Mrs Matthew's husband had died some years before, but she had the company of Dicky's best pal Bob and his sister Jean who were also evacuees. After tea Mrs Matthews would pound out a few notes to sing hymns to on her piano. She would like to have carried on all night but Uncle would have none of it. "I work all wik', includin' most of me' Sunday. I bin to Church, said me prayers, sang hymns an' listened to the reverend Mr Hurst. I inna agooin' yom (home) until weem 'ad a sing-song."

Mrs Matthews and Auntie would purse their lips, but say nothing as the youngsters dutiful but bored expressions changed. Uncle would pick up the old harmonium, that Mr Matthews used to play, from it's pride of place on the piano, play a couple of, out of tune, notes and launch into one of his several favourite music hall songs.

Mrs Matthews would grimace, as would Auntie, at the musical destruction and quickly join in, much to the delight of the kids who, by now, knew most of the words.

Sweet Rosie O'Grady
My beautiful Rose
She's my lovely lady
That everyone knows
Soon we will be married
My Rosie and me
Cos I love sweet Rosie O'Grady
And sweet Rosie O'Grady loves me

After about an hour of this and many other Music Hall favourites they would say their goodnights and make their way home. If it were dark, they would walk the long way round by road. If it were still light, they would take the short cut down the grass covered lane between farms, which led to the rear gated entrance to Uncle Bert's farm. This same path was used every Sunday by the Chapel visitors who lived on the topside of Woodmill and Jack's makeshift shanty was on the other side of the hedge in one of the Upton's fields, a little way up from the gate.

Jack died in the middle of a bad winter a few years after the end of the war. It was said that dozens of unopened pay packets were found sewn into the lining of his old greatcoat. His passing, no doubt generated an interest never there while he was alive. Did he have relatives? Was he ever married? Was he an ex-soldier? Where did he come from? What happened to the money?

Is it a bull?

The long winter gone. The usual Christmas in 'Brum' forgotten. The expected 2/- Postal Order for his birthday banked and the cows now permanently outside except for the milking time. It was now time to put another plan into action!

As promised, Bob came round a bit earlier than usual. He'd got sandwiches, a bottle of cold sweet tea, very refreshing on a warm early summer's day, such as it was and, more importantly, he'd brought the compass with him.

"Let's 'ave a look at it then" shouted Dicky. He'd already heard all about it, a present from Bob's brother who was in the RAF, but while home on leave had made time to come to Yoxall to see how his younger brother and sister Jean were. He'd also brought with him a model fighter plane, powered by winding and releasing an elastic band. He'd only finished making it the day before he came to visit and kept saying, "The glue hasn't had time to set yet. I'd give it a few days before trying it."

Over the next few weeks they'd tried it with various thicknesses of elastic band, each time fully wound up and held firmly before release. Each time the result was the same, more or less. Either one of them would release the wound up propeller and the plane exactly at the same time. The propeller would furiously rotate. The plane would vibrate, but just would not move along the flat, blue brick path, let alone take off.

Uncle Bert, who had been casually watching them whilst giving his pipe its weekly clean, had got up off the old wooden stool in the backyard of the farmhouse saying "Gie it 'ere lad, let's 'ave a look at it." He'd made sure the wheels were able to freely rotate. He'd turned it over and over and passed it from hand to hand, his large callused hands making it look like some sort of large butterfly.

"Reckon it's just too 'eavy" had been his judgement, passing it back and resuming his own personal battle with his pipe.

"That's it!" Bob had cried. "My brother said it would take off, then when the engine cuts out, it would glide to earth. Let's launch it from the top of the steps by the muck yard. C'mon!"

They'd galloped down the cottage path to the farmyard, the muckyard being at the farthest end away from the house. Not that its position made much difference to the thousands of flies that were a permanent part of livestock farms in the summer months. Uncle, now very interested, stuck his pipe in his pocket and followed them at a more leisurely pace. By the time he'd arrived alongside the muck-heap at the foot of the steps, Bob, having already climbed the steps and wound the propeller, was ready to launch the plane. Having made sure that Dicky and Uncle were in position to witness the historic event, he'd released the propeller, at the same time launching the plane outwards over the muck yard.

They'd figured that if the thing went down like a stone, it would have a soft landing without breaking up. But no! It had actually flown; well sort of, in a straight but descending line, until the engine cut out. Then the angle of descent got steeper and it had smashed into one of the fence uprights, breaking up completely.

"Told y' it were too 'eavy" Uncle had remarked, getting his pipe out and settling himself down at the foot of the steps to continue his weekly battle. And that had been the end of that.

Bob, with a flourish and a 'da, daah, da dah da dahh', held out his clasped hand and opened it. In the palm of his hand lay a small flat cylindrical object with a glass face. It was about 1" dia and about ?" thick.

"It's a bit small for a compass, innit?" Dicky said.

"Yeah, it 'as to be small 'cos it's what aircrew are issued with in case they're shot down over Germany. But it works. 'ere, you try it"

Dicky eagerly accepted the compass and started walking round in circles whilst watching it. "It's great, can your brother get me one."

"I dunno. I'll get Jean to ask 'im next time she writes." Bob continued, "Where's your grub an' that? We're gonna make an early start, aren't we?"

Dicky slung the bag containing his food and drink, around his shoulders and they both mounted their bikes and set off on their pre-planned adventure, the sole purpose of which was the discovery of the secret American Air Force base from which they could constantly hear planes taking off, destination unknown. The planes, which were obviously bombers, judging by the enormous racket they made, never flew over Woodmill or even Yoxall for that matter. But, also obviously to Dicky and Bob, they surely couldn't be more than 10 miles away. They had decided to set a course to the area the engine sounds were coming from and to go through thick and thin following the compass pointer once they had gone beyond Mr Yeomans farm on the 'top road' as it was called.

They pedalled the 3 miles to Yeomans farm and about another 2 miles past. The compass pointer was now pointing approximately NE, according to 'Bob the navigator', which meant climbing over the hedge into the field beyond and progressing on foot. Dicky, who'd insisted on being the driver of the 'search and destroy unit' because he hadn't got the compass, said "we'll have to leave our machines here and proceed on foot, keeping low and moving fast to avoid detection."

They found a narrow gap in the substantial hawthorn hedge, which was braced with sturdy timber fencing. They climbed over and dogtrotted, Red Indian style, up the slope of the field towards the high timber fence between them and the large wood from beyond which the roar of plane engines revving up was now much louder. About 100 yards from the fence they stopped, Bob to make an essential check on his compass. At the same time they both became aware of cattle bellowing in the field adjacent to the one they were in. A casual glance confirmed that it was just one beast on its own, but clearly upset about something. It was in line with them and about 20 yards the other side of the hedge that was about 100 yards from them. "Is it a bull? Bob enquired, in deference to Dicky's greater experience of farm life.

"I inna sure," replied Dicky, "I canna see a ring in its nose an' it inna built like a bull, but it dunna look very friendly."

The beast was poring the ground, tossing its head when suddenly it turned and started trotting down the field.

"There's a gap in the hedge at the bottom" shouted Bob. They both realised the awful possibility at the same time. Bull or cow, it was clearly annoyed at them and would soon be in the same field as them. In an instant they'd both weighed up their options. Up the field to a high fence of unknown possible difficulties chased by a faster moving animal, or back the way they had come, which they knew, towards the route the beast would take to try and intercept them.

Instinctively, they both knew the answer. "C'mon!" shouted Bob and they took off running as fast as they could, all thoughts of finding the Yankee airfield gone with the wind.

The beast reached the gap at the bottom and seeing that its quarry was about 50 yards from the safety of the road, picked up speed to a thundering charge alongside the hedge they were running towards. "Don't climb. JUMP!" gasped Dicky, with about 30 yards to go. They were almost side-by-side, heads back, legs pounding as fast as they could. The snorting, fast charging bull, its hooves kicking up clods of earth and grass, and now seeming 'ginormously' bigger, the ring in its nose clearly visible, was only yards away when Bob and Dicky simultaneously took off, cleared the timber fencing, continued running across the road and feverishly climbed the opposite high, deer proof, fence to safety, just in case.

The bull's charge had carried it well past the gap and unable now to see its quarry, lost interest in them. After a few minutes getting their breath and checking that the bull was now not a threat, Dicky and Bob collected their bikes and made their way homewards.

"I dropped my compass in that field" Bob said, somewhat ruefully.

"Are y' gunna go back forrit' then?" asked Dicky.

"Buggeroff!" replied Bob.

Tarzan and The Muckyard

It was Saturday afternoon towards the end of the summer. After an unusually long hot spell with no rain, everything was fairly quiet at Woodmill farm. Haymaking was finished. There would be no milling of corn for a few weeks yet. Hedging wouldn't start until autumn and the vegetable gardens were really down to selective picking and some tidying up, much of which Auntie did anyway.

There wasn't much for Dicky to do except help with the mucking out and the milking of the cows, also fetch and carry for Uncle Bert when necessary repairs to anything on the farm and mill were being done.

"You'm a fine workmate Dicky lad," Uncle would often say, "dunna know what I'd do wi'out yer" and he'd continue to hum, whistle or sing what few words he could remember of any old music hall song that fitted the tempo he was working at.

If he were chopping wood for kindling, it would almost always be the popular wartime song

> 'Run rabbit, run rabbit, chop, chop, chop!
> Here comes the farmer with his chop, chop. Chop!
> He'll get by, wi'out his rabbit pie.
> Run rabbit, run rabbit, chop, chop, chop'.

And when he was repairing something, which required patience and steadiness, he would often lapse into,

> 'If those eyes could only see, if those lips could only speak,
> I wouldn't have lasted a fortnit, and like as not even a week'.

The tune was the haunting refrain so popular for many years with a few of Uncle's words added. Sometimes, when confronted with something out of the ordinary, he would sing

> 'The strangest thing I ever did see.
> Was an elephant's nest in a rhubarb tree'.

Occasionally, of course, he would stop whatever he was doing, clean out his pipe, cut shavings of Black Twist tobacco, which he would then rub between thumb and the palm of his other hand, stuff and press the 'baccy' into his pipe prior to satisfactorily getting it alight after much sucking, puffing and 'tamping' down with callused thick skinned thumb whilst aiming and firing a mouthful of tobacco spit at a sunbathing bluebottle fly, much to Dicky's delight, especially if a hit was made. "One down, ten million to go" Uncle would say triumphantly.

From his position, sitting on top of the high brick wall skirting the steps up to the storeroom above the milking shed, Dicky watched and waited for his best pal Bob Mewis, another evacuee who, with his sister Jean, was staying with Mrs Matthews, a widow and relative of Uncle Bert. Her cottage was about a mile away and Bob, after finishing his chores, would usually cycle round after his midday meal. Fetching the cows in and milking them wouldn't start until about 5pm, so there would be around 4 hours to use up. Plenty of time for two lively, energetic and curious adventurers to fight imaginary foes, hunt imaginary wild animals, race each other across the fields, see who could jump the mill stream at various spots without getting their feet wet, make bows and arrows, climb inside the stationary wooden mill wheel and get it turning by 'walking' the 4' wide inner rim, dig for 'pig nuts', try the apples which were not full grown and ripe red yet.

"Ye'll get belly ache an' y' wunna want your supper then" would shout Auntie as she caught sight of them sneaking out of the orchard behind the chicken houses. Undeterred and giggling, the boys, always hungry, would retreat and eat the pocketed fruit.

Dicky didn't move from his position as Bob made his bumpy way down the dry, uneven farm driveway from the road. Loose stones and deep ruts severely impeding his progress, Bob would be turning the pedals furiously, determined to impress Dicky with his world beating effort to get to the winning line ahead of the horde of international racing cyclists behind him. He reached the line, braked and looked up grinning at Dicky, "wot y' doin' up there then."

Dicky stood up on top of the wall and said, "watch."

About 15' below him was the muckyard containing all the previous 12 months muck from the cowshed, the pigsty and the chicken sheds. Added to day by day, week by week, the heap, which started at the base of the wall Dicky was standing on, gradually got higher and spread further outwards until it eventually, as now, attained a mass about 5' high at its highest point and an area of about 12 square yards, enough to fill a double garage to about 4' deep. The bulk of it had a formed crust; dried by wind and sun to such an extent that Dicky could easily walk across the top. He'd previously tried jumping off the wall at several heights without breaking through the crust and was now ready to demonstrate his prowess to Bob.

Tarzan raised his arms above his 6'6" tall, gladiator like, body, his well-defined muscles glistening in the tropical humid heat of the African jungle. Throwing his magnificent maned head back and emitting his customary ferocious cry that resounded through the jungle escarpment, terrifying and causing the wildest animals to slink away for cover, he launched his supremely athletic body into space and landed quite comfortably on top of the sun baked pile of muck, his plimsoll clad feet hardly denting the crust.

Dicky looked across at Bob whose mouth was open and gleefully shouted "y' gunna 'ave a goo then?"

Bob, his face set in a determined manner, dropped the bike where it was, grabbed a nearby stick and poked at the manure crust from where he could reach it from a few steps up. Satisfied with the firm condition, he grinned again, ascended the steps and stood up on the top of the wall from where Dicky had launched himself.

"Looks bloody 'igh from up 'ere!" Bob exclaimed, his grin now having disappeared.

"Aw c'mon," yelled Dicky, "it inna like jumpin' on concrete. It sort of gives a bit, y'know."

Bob had come part way down the steps, climbed up again on to the steeply angled descending wall and was trying to steady himself at the awkward angle, "I'm gunna try it from 'ere fust. I know you. Youm probably bin practising at different heights too."

Dicky grinned and said nothing. He sat on the top bar of the farm fencing opposite and watched.

Bob grinned again. He had the ability and self-discipline to look quite serious and stern, seemingly at will, whereas Dicky and young Duggie were prone to fits of helpless giggling for very little reason. A grin was never far away from Bob's face though, especially when he was contemplating a 'dare'. He managed to steady himself and leapt out, landing quite comfortably on the crusted surface where his hobnailed boots left a distinct impression and indentation.

"That were great", he yelled "nowt to it." His face flushed and grinning, he walked off the muckheap and ran up the steps two at a time, mounted the wall and stood, arms raised, preparing to jump. "Blimey! It still looks bloody 'igh" he muttered. "Right, 'ere goes." He, like Dicky, gave out a strangulated cry that had the farmyard chickens briefly worried, then leapt outwards.

Down he came, legs straight and stiff. His leather hobnailed boots went straight through the crust; followed by about 10" inches of each leg, his progress downwards only being halted by him overbalancing backwards and sitting down on the, still substantial, crust.

"Crikey!" exclaimed Dicky; practically falling off the fence in his excitement and desire to see what mess Bob was in. Laughing almost fit to burst, Dicky clambered up by the side of Bob, who was unsuccessfully trying to extricate himself.

"I canna move me bloody legs at all" he yelped.

"Phwaw! What a stink". The stench of released gas from the putrefying manure was fast enveloping them both and Dicky, who thought he had experienced every type of farmyard smell, was for the first time savouring the stench of 'well rotted' manure, a smell he would never forget.

Dicky had got both of his arms around one of Bob's legs above the knee and was pulling upwards to no avail. The leg would not budge and the trapped softer manure, trying to escape from the pressure above, was now starting to form a glutinous collar around each of Bob's legs above the level of the crust and edging towards Dicky's plimsolls. "I'll 'ave to get Uncle" muttered Dicky and quickly retreated to look for him.

Uncle Bert, not too pleased at being awakened from his afternoon snooze, grumpily arrived, took one look, got the general picture and quickly regained his normal good-natured composure. He made his way to the bottom of the steps, chuckling and feeling for his pipe, and sat down.

Being a big man, he could comfortably see over the wall. "Youm in the muck there lad and that's a fact." He tapped his pipe on the wall and got to work with his penknife scraping out the bowl to his

161

satisfaction, then quite languidly proceeded to prepare and stuff his 'baccy' in the pipe before the 'time honoured' procedure of 'getting' the 'owd bloody thing a'gooin'.

"Can you get me out Uncle?" wailed Bob, not sure now whether to grin or not.

"I 'ope youm got your bootlaces tied well and tight" remarked Uncle and spat a long steady stream of tobacco saliva at two flies mating on the sun warmed wall.

"Damnation, missed" he muttered as the joined up pair flew off unscathed. "Weem got a bit o' thinkin' to do 'ere, an' that's a fact. I canna get up there wi' you. I maun be three times your weight an' I bin in enough of that stuff already to last me the rest of my life." He chuckled "inna no 'urry is there lad?"

With his, seemingly asbestos covered, thumb, he again tamped down the burning tobacco, a look of amused concern on his face. "Mmmmn, yep! we'll 'ave to get some plankin' an you Dicky lad, go an' put your wellies on an' fetch the smallest spade we'm got."

Uncle Bert, chuckling and shaking his head, went off to the woodshed, the strains of his 'rhubarb' song drifting back on the gentle breeze. He soon returned with several short planks and one about 15' long, Dicky not far behind.

"E'yar Dicky lad, get up there an' I'll pass these planks up to y'. Tek the spade with you." Dicky clambered up, his nose now more or less accustomed to the rank smell.

"Right Dicky, put one of the short planks behind Bob for him to sit on and one in front, level with the first one, with a gap of about 15". Now put two short planks, one either side o' Bob about 18" apart and on top of the ends of the 2 planks already there."

Uncle waited until Dicky had got the planks in the desired positions, then continued, "now Dicky lad, we want this long plank under Bob's legs, just be'ind 'is knees, and the end of it on top of the plank on the right side of Bob."

Uncle studied the set-up and, satisfied with the arrangement, lifted his end of the longer plank until he'd got the weight of Bob on it.

"Right Dicky lad, you stand on the plank in front of Bob and break up the crust at the front and sides of 'is legs. Careful you dinna chop one of 'em off. Then shovel out as much of the muck as y'can while I try an' lever 'im out."

Dicky, quite accustomed to spade work around the farm and gardens did as he was told, while Uncle applied an increasing effort to lifting his end of the plank. After a bit of initial resistance, Bob's legs and boots slowly emerged, totally unrecognisable underneath the mess of coagulated very 'ripe' manure.

He lifted his legs clear, swung around and joyfully stood up, mightily relieved. "Thanks Uncle," he grinned and walked stiff legged, feet well apart off the heap.

"Youm best carry on walkin' to the stream." Uncle called out to Bob, "an' gi' y' legs boots and feet a good weshin'. Then come back and clean yersen under the pump. You an' all Dicky. Christ! you stink, the pair on yer. Then y'can put the planks an' wood an' shovel back where they belong."

He strode off carrying the long plank, chuckling. It would be a good story, all the better for telling and retelling.

Moving Times, 1943

The summer months were rolling by and everything was happening in Europe. All the grown ups were talking about the war being over soon. German and Italian forces had surrendered in North Africa. Allied troops had landed in Sicily. British and American Air Forces were stepping up their bombing campaign over Germany. The Russian Red Army was proving to be indomitable and starting to drive the German forces back. The Italian Dictator Mussolini was arrested and Italy instigated peace negotiations.

Meanwhile, down on the farm, where the cacophony of noise created by the beating wings of thousands of insects, occasionally interrupted by the triumphant clucking made by one of the hens, after producing her umpteenth miracle birth in as many days, a new sound entered the fray. Nellie was the first to hear and getting to her feet, gave one bark, her tail slowly wagging. Dicky, from his favourite 'lookout post', sitting at the top of the steps, on the wall above the muck-heap, his sense of smell now completely inured to all livestock and agricultural aromas, heard Nellie's bark and recognised the warning of a vehicle's approach. He instantly knew it was a regular visitor because, although he could see or hear nothing, he knew and trusted Nellie's superior hearing, which was soon justified. The little black Austin car, driven by Kathy Buchanan, one of 'Pop' Lester's married daughters, turned into the farm drive and wended it's uncertain path along and over the stone walled bridge, its narrow tyred wheels protesting as they juddered from side to side on the rutted and stony surface.

Dicky didn't see her very often, normally being at school when she delivered the paper and his Wizard comic. But she was as regular as Mr Simpkin, the butcher. As regular as Jack and his milk lorry. As regular as the seasons, feeding stock, preparing fields, milking cows, harvesting produce. As regular as paying the rent every three months, up at the hall at Hoar Cross. Touch of forelock and 'mornin sir' to the polite, smart suited gentleman sitting behind the table, brought out into the yard for the occasion. Everything in its seasonally ordered, steadily paced way.

Dicky had long given up on the possibility of seeing any enemy troops, apart from the occasional Italian prisoner of war working as a farm labourer. They always seemed friendly and would shout and wave as they went by in the trucks on the way to the fields. There were rarely aircraft flying over Woodmill, although the noise of aircraft engines could be heard when the wind was blowing in a certain direction, presumably from the American base about 10 miles away.

In the absence of his best pal Bob Mewis, the only other lad of his age nearby was Pete Sharratt, who lived in one of the cottages almost opposite the farm drive. If Pete wasn't around then it was down to Dicky's own imagination and The Wizard, his big favourite being Wilson, the strange man who'd dedicated his life to discipline, hardship and physical training on the northern moors, where he had met an ancient hermit who'd given him the secret elixir of life.

The weekly stories of physical 'epics' in a variety of circumstances would inspire Dicky to pretend he was Wilson as he ran, climbed, jumped or pretended to be a buffalo wrestler as he twisted the baby horns on Marie's head, forcing her to the ground. The fact that Marie was only a few weeks old helped of course. But as she got older and ran up to Dicky to play, it soon became too one-sided in her favour and Dicky would have to take evasive action, pretty damn quick too! And later, she would be the only cow that Dicky wouldn't dare try and milk. In her playfulness, Marie was now more of a threat to Dicky's long-term health, than your average bull.

Dicky had, for some time now, been cycling to school and further afield, even to Dunstall village where Duggie had still been staying with the 'biscuit lady'. Dicky's mother had wondered if Duggie would be allowed to move over to Woodmill, so they would both be together. Everyone seemed happy about it, so it happened and Duggie caught the bus to Yoxall, where he was met by Dicky and introduced to farming life and little jobs like feeding the hens and helping Auntie. Not that he had to do much, he was only 9 years old and messed things up for Dicky, who had not foreseen that he would have to walk to school again, accompanying Duggie.

There was a bonus though, as invariably there is in most changed circumstances, of which there had been plenty in Dicky's young life. He and young Duggie frequently joined up with other groups of kids walking to school and back home along the road now used with increasing frequency by fleets of trucks carrying American troops. This, no doubt, was the beginning of the big 'build up' of allied forces and equipment, prior to the invasion of 'Nazi' controlled Europe. Not that anyone in Yoxall would know that. The American drivers, no doubt mindful of the fact there were rarely any footpaths on country lanes, drove accordingly, giving time for plenty of two way 'banter' and the occasional successful results to the shouts of "Got any gum, chum?"

The car stopped and Nellie, her tail wagging so furiously she could hardly walk, her extended nose high, desperately searching for the slightest whiff of something, anything she could grab and trot round the back of the barn with, moved towards the emerging figure of Kathy Buchanan. Kathy, her one hand holding the newspaper and Dicky's comic, extended her free hand for Nellie to sniff at saying, "sorry Nellie, nothing today."

She patted the disappointed dog's head, not too disappointed that the tail stopped wagging completely as Nellie followed Kathy and Dicky towards the farm cottage. And certainly not that miserable that she didn't want to chase after Dicky, who, comic in one hand, raced back to the farmyard and his favourite position on top of the wall. The dog, fully aware of Dicky's preferred spot, was there first, already in her regular reclined position, both front feet hanging over the top step, her head raised, her panting mouth wide open, in what appeared to the panting Dicky, a triumphant grin. Nellie didn't know there was a war on!

Indians and Bullets

The Monday mornings' work 'tater pickin' had finished, the lunchtime sandwiches and cold tea had been consumed, which didn't take the youngsters, who were keen to forage in the adjacent woods, more than a few minutes. Excitedly yelling, the group of about thirty boys and girls spread out and charged into the trees, each one eager to be the first to catch sight of any telltale proof of the British plane rumoured to have crashed a couple of nights previously.

All of the 'Brummie' evacuees had experienced the excitement and terror of German air raids and the subsequent 'trophy finds'. Shrapnel from exploding anti-aircraft shells, tailfins from incendiary bombs, bits of disintegrating enemy aircraft, barrage balloons and far flung debris from bomb damaged buildings. Rich pickings indeed, resulting in a somewhat macabre swap culture infinitely more interesting than weekly comic magazines.

The village kids were jealous of the 'Brummies' tales of glory, the air raid sirens, the all-night raids, the drone of the German bombers engines, the terrifying scream of bombs hurtling downwards and the subsequent awful silence as the helpless listeners waited for the explosion. Those that didn't hear it were most likely already and immediately dead. The nightly sessions in the air raid shelters, the near misses, the total support and co-operation of the lucky survivors towards the not so lucky. More than one village kid had scrounged a spare 'trophy' off an evacuee, but it just wasn't the same and they couldn't appreciate the reality.

There was no TV; most village kids never had the chance to visit a cinema, the nearest being in Burton, 10 miles away. Newspapers were available in the village shop, which were often visited only once weekly by outlying villagers, so much current knowledge was learned off the BBC Radio Home Service, or by word of mouth, often initiated by the driver of the milk collection lorry during his round collecting the milk from all the local farms and transporting it to the Midland Counties Dairies in Birmingham.

The low calls and whistles of the searching band of North American Indian scouts as their moccasin clad feet padded swiftly through the forest

checking for broken branches and other signs of disturbance, suddenly
changed to excited yelps of discovery, only to be as suddenly muted by the
scene of utter devastation opened up before them.

There was little recognisable left of the Wellington twin-engine
bomber, which had obviously burnt out. The impact and presumed
explosion had flung debris in all directions away from the grey ash
and smoke blackened remains of the plane fuselage and it was
obvious that RAF personnel and available rescue services had
scoured the area, removing remains of armaments and of the crew
members who had perished.

The kids however, were in luck. Their feverish 'picking over'
with much sharper eyes and closer to the ground, had gleaned
various 'trophies'. Nothing whole, but many partly burnt remains of
sheepskin lined leather flying jackets, leather helmets, goggles,
strapping, buckles, remains of a flying boot with what appeared to be
the gruesome remains of a foot inside, bits of equipment smashed
and partly burnt in the conflagration, all that was left after the 'clean
up' job by the authorities earlier. And then, as they spread out from
the plane remains, the big prize was found, LIVE AMMUNITION!
Dozens of rounds of unexploded cannon shells from the plane's
machine guns obviously flung far and wide in the explosion and
missed by the earlier searchers. The more they searched the more
they found, and all the boys, the girls weren't interested, took home,
carefully concealed, several rounds each.

No one must know. This was to be their big secret. All evacuees
and locals agreed, this was an equalising event, much better than the
discomfort of air raid shelters, although most kids, under the age of
14, thought war was adventurous fun. Just a more realistic series of
the sort of events they had been reading about for years in various
comics. Only when family members and neighbours were tragically
affected, did the real seriousness of war strike home, devastatingly
so.

The remaining 'tater pickin' period passed by without much
excitement, so necessary for most kids, and school recommenced.
Because of the much colder temperature in winter, a large fire would
be well alight in the main classroom before the children arrived. The
large dividing curtains would be drawn back and in severe weather,
room would be made for the infants, their classroom, like the rest of

the school, being reliant on old water filled radiators served by an equally old and cantankerous boiler, sometimes!

On these occasions, adjustments would be made and all children, seniors, juniors and infants would be 'taught' in the same large room. Any semblance of advanced learning was not particularly essential at St Peters school, Yoxall, in this period of uncertainty and chaos.

On one of these 'all together' occasions, newly married Mrs Ward, formerly Miss Baker, confiscated something that Pete Sharratt was tapping on his desk, much to her annoyance. She snatched 'it' and threw 'it' into the fire blazing behind her. This 'it', the older kids knew to be a 'live' round from the recently crashed Wellington bomber. Whilst Mrs Ward tried to continue her lesson, the kids were all expectantly waiting to see, in their childish ignorance, what would happen next.

They didn't have to wait long. There was a loud crack, a splintering of a desktop and the bullet ricocheted elsewhere, fortunately not hitting anyone. The kids were amazed and excited. Mrs Ward was terrified and in no time at all, the local village constable, PC Northwood, was at the school collecting names of all those who had got ammunition, Dicky included.

Next day, PC Northwood accompanied by 'Uncle', Special Constable Bert Roe, went around all the addresses collecting the ammunition, possibly to pass on to the local Commander of the illustrious Home Guard, the .303 bullets ideally suited for their 'own' Bren Gun, they would now be able to practise with 'for real'.

Meanwhile after again buying footwear for Duggie and himself, Dicky had banked almost £9 in his Racing Bike saving book. Would it be enough?

Going Home

Christmas has come and gone in its customary fashion and it was now Friday 4th February 1944, Dicky's 14th birthday and the day it was agreed that Dicky could leave school and return home to Birmingham. More importantly, he was now legally old enough to start work and earn some very necessary money for a largish family, with a father of doubtful health. Billy Blood, who had served in the Royal Navy in the first World War, the British Army overseas for several years in the 1920's and invalided out of the RAF during the early part of the Second World War, due, in part, to the severe health problems that had nearly killed him in the 1930's and caused him major employment problems for years, had been directed to a deskbound job at BSA, as a clerk, on pay very much less than Dolly Blood was earning on night work at the Austin works.

Billy Blood resented this in every way. Not only was he niggled that his wife's work was much more important and better paid than his, he was also of the old school that considered a woman's place was in the home. Housework, raising the kids, making sure his meals were ready and that his clothes were clean and pressed for any occasion. He'd help with any decorating and with the garden, which he much rather preferred to sit in, in the sun of course.

Because Dolly was on nights and rarely got home before 9am, very tired, it was left to Dad and Maurice to sort out Barry and Laurence and make sure they'd had breakfast and were ready for school, before they themselves left for work. This was a problem, as they both started work at 8am and had to leave the house about 7.30 am. This unsatisfactory situation could not continue much longer. Mrs Blood was 42 years of age, three months into her 6th pregnancy and wouldn't be able to stay at work much longer. Dicky's starting wage wouldn't be much, but it would alleviate the loss of her wages a little. Tough as she was, she probably felt that she'd done her share for the war effort. Over three years working nights, producing armaments while being bombed some of the time, also coping with a family etc., was no mean feat, but no different to the sacrifices most other adults were making, many fatally so.

The extra money earned during those war years had been put to good use. Dicky had returned home each Christmas for a few days, also once during the summer. On each visit he'd noticed little changes and improvements. The old second hand basic furniture had been replaced and all rooms were now adequately furnished, even the once empty front room, which was sometimes let' to lodgers down on their luck, nothing unusual on most council estates before the war, when unemployment was rife.

New fireplaces had been installed in both living rooms by the landlord, the local council, and in all rooms there were now better looking curtains, behind which still lurked the old blackout curtains, ready and waiting to be drawn thereby hiding the sticky taped window panes. There was even new linoleum on every floor, but no carpets anywhere. Blue-collar workers, even those in regular employment, would be hard pushed to afford a carpet, let alone fitted ones. It wasn't until Cyril Lord in the 1950's revolutionised the carpet trade, by mass producing very cheaply and selling 'direct to the public', that things altered and made fitted carpets much more affordable.

Pride of place in the newly furnished front room was a glass fronted display cabinet in which Dolly Blood had placed weirdly shaped pieces of aluminium 'scrap' she'd brought home from work, amongst other personal possessions and small framed photographs.

Dolly Blood would have thought that her house was now as good as anyone else's in the area and would be happy about that. She certainly would not want to be better than anyone else. It just wasn't her nature. But now she'd be happy to give up work and concentrate on the family, which would please Billy Blood and Maurice no end.

Dicky had packed his few possessions and spare clothes in the old suitcase given to him by Mr Armson two years previously and lugged them the one mile to school that morning. His bike would remain, as a present, to Duggie, who would be staying on at Woodmill. With his 'tater pickin' money and other bits of money he'd saved, Dicky intended buying a new bicycle, similar to the one he'd fancied all those years ago. The one in Priory Road Cycle shop. The RACING bike!

His mother was travelling from Birmingham to collect him and take him home, a two to three hour journey by bus. With an early start, no problem, as still working nightshifts she could start out when she left work and 'nap' on the three different buses she would need to use, she expected to arrive at the school around 11am. This would give Mrs Ward sufficient time to complete his school-leaving certificate, which proclaimed that his Arithmetic, English, attendance and behaviour were good. The Head teacher's comment was 'this pupil should go far', a very prophetic comment.

His mother arrived, Dicky said his goodbyes and armed with the certificate that would ensure his future, they left to board the Green bus, which duly arrived, more or less on time.

The journey home was uneventful, apart from the amazement shown by the conductress when Mrs Blood told her that Dicky had left school and was going home to start work.

"Why, 'e's only a little lad an' still in short trousers. 'e dunna look old enough."

Mortified and blushing, Dicky tried to make himself look bigger, but to no avail.

"Never mind", the conductress continued, "Goodness comes in small parcels."

"Aye! And so does poison," replied his mom. Both women chuckled and Dicky was left to himself as they chatted, his mind full of expectancy and uncertainties.

They changed buses in Lichfield, where they had fish and chips and a cup of tea before continuing homewards. Another bus change in Birmingham and finally the bus deposited them at Trittiford Park at the bottom of School Road hill, a quarter of a mile from home at the top of the hill. They passed the entrance of Yardley Wood School just as the kids were leaving for home at the end of the day's lessons. There were hundreds of them, juniors and seniors, many of them much bigger and older looking than Dicky, who felt somewhat overwhelmed by the sheer numbers of playing, shouting kids making their way home. He recognised none and no-one recognised him.

He suddenly felt alone and for the first time in his life, wondered about the future and what sort of job he was going to start on Monday, subject to the required visit to Birmingham Labour Exchange tomorrow, from whence all labour was directed, as and when it became available, a wartime government dictate.

He unexpectedly felt homesick for the farm and Uncle and Auntie. By the evening though, everything had changed and so had his feelings. The kids, Barry and Laurence, were already home from school and clamoured about him excitedly. Maurice arrived home from his job as a trainee plumber. He was still wearing his dirty and greasy overalls, understandable in the winter and still had his trusty 'Dawes' cycle.

He would be 16 years of age on March 21st and intended to join the Royal Navy as a boy entrant. He now seemed very grown up and was smoking, as he had been since he was about 12 years of age, surreptitiously of course, but just like most kids. No anti-smoking lobbies or health warnings then.

Maurice checked Dicky's height against the wall. "Wassa marrer with ya! You've 'ardly bleedin' moved. You're about 8 inches be'ind me now!"

"Piss off!" replied Dicky, not wishing to be reminded of what was so painfully obvious.

Some of Dicky's old pals were soon round to see if he could 'come out to play' and great sport was made of his 'country' accent, which to them sounded funny, just as it had every time he'd come home for a few days holiday. In no time at all, most of the kids in that part of School Road were out and gathered around Dicky. Joyce Bentley, his once possible sweetheart to be, shyly smiled and acknowledged him. Dicky, even shyer, smiled and returned the gesture. They remained just good pals.

"Ain't ya wearin' longuns yet?" was the oft repeated question by his pals, all wearing long trousers.

It had never been a problem to Dicky before as most of the village kids his age wore short trousers, even his best mate Bob Mewis who was much taller, bigger and destined to be Yoxall's blacksmith.

"I inna got any yet, but I maun gettin' some t'morra," Dicky replied and grinned at their laughing and mimicry of his odd accent.

Next morning, Mrs Blood and Dicky were up and on the bus to town before 8am. Dolly Blood wanted to make sure they got to the Labour Exchange early, before a queue had time to form. Dicky had wanted to get his long trousers first as he thought it might make him look a bit bigger, but his Mom had reasoned that it would be best to know what sort of job he'd been given, as it would decide what overalls, if any, he would need.

Dolly Blood's forethought paid off, as they were at the head of the small queue when the doors opened and they were directed through to a large room where a formidable looking, soberly dressed gentleman was standing behind a pulpit type, high desk, studying a large open ledger on the desk top.

"C'mon then, up 'ere lad," he said as he motioned with his free hand, the other hand marking the spot he was studying.

After adding Dicky's name and address to the ledger he asked, "so what do you want to be then? A plumber, a machine operator, a coalminer?" He smiled then continued, "Or a jockey?"

Dolly Blood also smiled, but Dicky; now red-faced, stammered, "I want to be a carpenter and joiner."

He really hadn't a clue what he wanted to be, as careers and any sort of employment guidance just weren't on the agenda at St Peters School, Yoxall. Maybe it was because it didn't matter much at a school where most kids were likely to follow in their father's footsteps on the land. Maybe it was because of the uncertainty of war. Whatever, most kids of Dicky's age, who were not going on to grammar school or private education or similar, thought only of leaving school, getting some sort of job and earning a bit of money, some of which they would be able to keep to save towards the sort of things most kids desired, – A better bike, even if second-hand, a penknife or scout knife, an air pistol or rifle. How times have changed! No doubt the girls had different preferences, but the 'career forward planning' was the same. Leave school, get a job and for the first time in their lives, have some money to spend and save.

"A carpenter and joiner eh," the man said and continued "Well, let's have a look then."

He reached under the desk, brought out another ledger, opened it and with a dexterity that belied his demeanour, ruffled rapidly through the pages until, with an extravagant movement, he slammed down his hand onto the open pages. "I knew it!" he cried, "right here where I thought it was, just the job for you," he paused for effect, "especially for you, young man."

Mrs Blood moved forward. "What's it say then?"

"It says boy wanted. What do you want it to say?" replied the man.

"Well, will 'e get trainin' an' that?" Asked Mrs Blood.

"If he's a good lad and behaves himself, of course he'll get trained." The important man was now writing out the address, which he then gave to Mrs Blood. "Alfred Davis, Packing Case Makers, Moseley Road, Balsall Heath or Moseley, it says here, probably not sure where it is because of the bombing."

"I know exactly where it is," said Mrs Blood, "we used to live opposite St Paul's church, next door to Davis's place."

"Very good, then your lad will have no problem finding it, will he?" He paused briefly and continued "8am Monday morning and don't be late."

He banged his right hand down on a desk bell, put the second ledger away and was already looking at the first ledger before Dolly Blood and Dicky started moving for the door, which was now open and admitting a couple of nervous looking young women. As she passed them, Dolly Blood whispered "bloody show-off, thinks 'e's God almighty."

One of the girls giggled. Dicky didn't, as he was trying to get used to the fact that he'd got a job and that by next Friday he would have his first pay packet.

By an odd coincidence their next destination that morning, was the same Moseley Road, to buy some long trousers and bib and brace overalls from an outfitters Mrs Blood had been using for years. The proprietor was one of the many credit drapers in Birmingham, and by an even stranger coincidence, his name was Mr Yoxall and his shop was almost opposite Alfred Davis, Packing Case Maker. In a big city like Birmingham, that was a very strange coincidence.

A little further along the same road was a cycle shop. Dicky had exactly £9 saved in the Post Office and wanted to see what he could buy 'NEW'. He was, however, disappointed. The man said he didn't sell racing bikes, which were very expensive, but he had a nice range of touring and general-purpose bikes to choose from. Unfortunately, £9.13s (£9.65p) was the cheapest new one, so Dicky came away from the shop disappointed and now not very hopeful of getting a racing bike.

On the same Saturday afternoon, after dinner (lunch, 'Brummies' midday meal was always referred to as dinner,) Dicky put on his new grey flannel 'longuns' and got Maurice's bike out to ride round to Priory Cycles.

"You get chain oil on them new trousers an' you'll be in big trouble" yelled his Mom.

Dicky just grinned. He knew that he hadn't been home long enough yet for his Mom to be really cross with him, but all the same he tucked his trousers into the long socks he was still wearing. Priory Cycles had several makes of racing bikes, all very expensive and way out of Dicky's reach. Even a second hand one would cost more than he'd got and he'd promised himself a new bike anyway.

Oh well! That was that and Dicky promptly gave up on the idea, especially when the man in Priory Cycles told him that getting a racing bike was only the start. He'd need special shoes, clothes, gloves, wheel, tube and tyre spares, repair kit, subscription to a club and more importantly, he needed to grow a bit.

"Come back in a few years time, when you're a bit bigger and stronger" the man said.

Dicky cycled home wondering how many weeks it would take him to save the extra 13s (65p) required to purchase the ordinary 'general purpose' bike. The racing bike was now history.

The following morning, Sunday, Dicky had not woken as early as usual, probably because he'd had two late nights in succession. Town kids definitely stayed up later than country kids, in Dicky's experience. He couldn't imagine many town kids regularly getting up at 6am to milk cows before breakfast and a mile walk to school as well.

Dolly Blood was up and cleaning the ashes out of the new fireplace when Dicky came down. It was still early, but not for Dolly. She somehow managed on very little sleep and in normal times was always up very early.

"Here's your birthday present son" she said and pulled a £1 note out of her overall pocket. "I know it's two days late, but y'can get that bike now."

"Thanks Mom!" Dicky shouted, overjoyed. It was the most money, by far, that he'd ever received as a gift. He could now go into the cycle shop on Moseley Road and pay for the bike on Monday the day he was starting work, providing he could find a nearby Post Office to cash in his savings book.

Starting work - February 1944

Monday morning and it was snowing with intent, big flakes steadily falling and settling, the ground too cold to thaw. Billy Blood, Maurice and Dicky were up and away before 7.30am, carrying the sandwiches prepared and bagged by Dolly Blood the night before. Maurice had shouted as he left on his bike "fust day at werk ar kid? Watch out for tricks," then he was off, head down against the flurry of falling snow. Dicky and his Dad took the same bus, 13a, to Stratford Road, where they both changed buses to the inner circle No 8, Dad going eastwards to the BSA and Dicky going in the opposite direction to Moseley Road, where he got off and ran the four or five hundred yards to his new place of employment, hampered by the snow and his new long trousers and overalls, both of which had had the legs turned up and sewn by the Blood's neighbour, Mrs Bentley.

"You're late, an' on the first day too. I s'pose you're the new kid starting today?" The voice came from the small office on Dicky's right as he entered the premises.

The question was more a statement made by Billy Moore, the foreman at Alfred Davis, obviously noting Dicky was wearing new overalls. "15 minutes late. Not a very promisin' start and don't give me any excuse about snow. I was 'ere on time and so was everyone else. I'll let you off this time, but remember this. 16 minutes late and you lose 'arf 'ours pay. 'Arf 'our late an' you lose one 'ours pay".

He looked Dicky over for a couple of seconds, grunted, turned round and walked quickly away, stopping after a few steps to shout at Dicky, who hadn't moved. "C'mon then, where d'you think you bloody well are, waitin' forra bus or summat?"

Dicky quickly ran after the foreman through some big swing doors into a large area containing several men working at benches and a variety of woodworking machines, saws and planers. At the one end there were large swing doors through which Dicky could see an open yard containing a massive circular saw ripping its way through an equally massive log secured to the saw bench gradually moving towards the screaming saw. One man appeared to be in charge of this

177

operation, with a young lad seemingly banging wedges into the sawcut slot.

The foreman stopped by another man, operating a suspended swinging crosscut saw, who stopped work when the foreman indicated he wanted to speak to him. He briefly introduced Dicky as the new lad, said, "Keep y'eye on 'im an' keep 'im busy, 'e already owes us 15 minutes."

Then he was off, no doubt to pursue his responsibility as the Firm's chief whip and co-ordinator of the labour force, a man of considerable power, respected by his skilled workers and feared by the youngsters, as yet, too young to be called up for military service. Jack, the crosscut saw operator pointed to a double row of coat hooks fixed to a nearby inside wall and said "'ang y'coat there lad, then collect an' stack the wood I'm cuttin' an' keep clear o'me while I'm workin'."

He then carried on his work, feeding through the long lengths of timber, to be clamped, then cut, at the required much shorter lengths, every now and then glancing across at Dicky, who had soon grasped the simplicity of his particular function and was enthusiastically keen to improve his first negative impression on Billy Moore.

'Collect and stack, collect and stack'. That was all Dicky did on his first day, apart from two ten-minute breaks for tea and a one-hour break for lunch. His immediate boss, Jack, had introduced Dicky to the rest of the workforce, five or six men, all too old for military service, several women and about a dozen boys, the youngest, apart from Dicky, being a lad that had also started work recently. Tea breaks were spent sitting around an iron stove, kept fiercely hot by numerous 'stokings' of timber offcuts, of which there were always plenty. At lunchtime, most adult workers went to their nearby homes for dinner and the kids, all of whom had brought sandwiches, remained, to quickly consume their 'grub' and then decide on their lunchtime activity for that day.

This particular day presented no problem. After quickly 'interrogating' Dicky and 'taking the mickey' out of his accent, whilst, at the same time 'wolfing down' their food, they frog marched Dicky outside into the yard, then up some wooden steps to a small platform outside a closed door. There the small party of three stopped, the remainder, expectantly gleeful, remaining at the bottom of the steps. One of the two big lads firmly gripping Dicky's arms said, "This is your fust day initiation ceremony. If you cry," he paused for effect, "then you 'as to do it agin', an agin'. If you don't cry, then you've passed. Gorrit?"

Before Dicky had time to say anything, one of the lads reached forward, yanked the door open and both lads easily propelled the much smaller boy through into the pitch-blackness beyond. Breathless and speechless in his terror and aware of the door slamming shut behind him, Dicky, unable to stop his forward momentum, felt himself falling almost headlong into black nothingness. After what seemed an eternity, but was probably less than one second, Dicky landed in something dry, dusty and thankfully soft. By the feel and smell of the stuff in his face and mouth, he realised it was sawdust. He was trying to extricate his arms, knees and the rest of his body partly buried in the stuff, when a door opened in the side of the building at just below his level. Through the daylight, now pouring in, Dicky could see one of the other lads. "Out 'ere Dicky, afore Billy Moore comes an' ketches us. Shake orf the sawdust fust."

Dicky laboriously made his way, lifting high one foot after another, to the lower edges of the gigantic pile of sawdust, then jumped up and down on the concrete floor until most of the clinging stuff had been shaken loose. Grinning, his recent terror now forgotten, he emerged from the 'cyclone pit', to be greeted with a reception of jeers and a barrage of small pieces of wood and bark. As none of the missiles were big enough to cause any real pain, Dicky, quickly and enthusiastically, responded.

This was more like it; this was what he loved, as did all the other boys, some of who soon sided with Dicky to make a better 'battle' of it. All too soon, the 'back to work' hooter sounded and Dicky was already thinking that 'this going to work lark' was OK. He was going to love it and he was going to get paid as well. What could be better? Only a brand new bike, which he bought the very next day with his Post Office savings and his Mom's birthday gift of one pound. He spent some of the remaining seven shillings (35p) on a pair of cycle trouser clips, a puncture repair kit and a cheap rain cape.

From thereon he would always use his bike for travelling to and from work, just like many thousands of other workers, young and not so young, male and female, all negotiating potholes, past temporarily repaired bomb craters, tram lines, the hundreds of double decker buses stopping at and pulling away from the many strategically placed bus 'request' stops, many of course, near converging or crossing routes. There would always be a few 'big bosses' private cars and taxis, but at least 99% of all 'Brum' residents would use trains, buses, bikes or walk to get to their place of work and history would prove they were healthier and fitter for it.

A few days later and still in his first week, Dicky was now conversant with most duties he was expected to fulfil. Carrying and stacking various uniform sizes of cut timber. Filling sacks with sawdust in the 'cyclone pit', the collection point for the sawdust vacuum-collected from all the wood machinery. Carrying and stacking recently delivered planks, after he'd strapped on a leather shoulder pad, obviously made 'one size only', for protection. And generally being at the 'beck and call' of everyone older than himself. On the Friday dinner-time break, he and the next youngest lad decided to climb over the high fencing separating the woodyard from the railway.

They clambered down to the side of the rails, their intention being to see if they could find anything interesting, something accidentally dropped or thrown out, maybe some shrapnel, although there hadn't been an air raid for some time now. No luck! There was nothing untoward. Just rails firmly secured to sleepers, which were just as firmly secured to the ground amid a bed of stones, some of which the lads started to throw about in frustration. It wasn't many minutes before they were seen and despite their successful efforts to 'escape' back over the fence, they were soon tracked and apprehended by the railway police, who handed them over to Billy Moore. He promptly sacked the lad who'd been an employee for only two weeks and gave Dicky a good telling off and a promise that just one more caper would be the sack for him too. Dicky was grateful to receive his first week's wage of £1, less 'stamp' stoppage of 9d (4p), the following Saturday morning.

Tea Boy and a Splitting Headache

It was Saturday morning and the last day of Dicky's first week at work. Mindful of how close he had been to losing his job the previous Wednesday, Dicky was at work well before 8am. He already knew this was the day he would start his new duties as 'teaboy', being the youngest employee and now responsible for fetching the break-time tea for the rest of the workers at Alfred Davis's, in place of the boy who'd been sacked the previous day. He would have taken over the chore the following Monday anyway, as the unwritten rule was that the most recent new boy took over the job on his second Monday with the firm.

Dicky had to collect up all the unwashed tin mugs that had been left near the stove, already lit by one of the older workers, wash them and place them upside down on a cleanish piece of lino nailed to a nearby bench. He then had to ask the twenty or so workers if they wanted anything with their tea, which cost two pence (1p) a mug, butter or beef dripping toast or oat flake flapjack, again usually two pence (1p) each. That was the choice, which he would then order from the café across the road.

Just before the 10am tea break, Dicky would take the massive two-handled red teapot, already cleaned out by him, across to the café and leave it there, to be filled with the required quantity of tea while he returned with the 'bagged' toast and biscuits etc. He would then gallop back to collect the teapot and return as quickly as possible, without spilling any of the contents, which included two spoonfuls of sugar for each mug. In those days, Dicky wasn't aware of anyone who didn't take sugar in their hot tea and real coffee was rarely the choice of manual workers. 'Camp coffee extract', though, was quite popular in 'working class' homes. After pouring the tea and making sure the 'grub' went to the ones who had ordered it, Dicky could sit down and enjoy his tea and 'grub', usually half the sandwiches his Mom had prepared for him.

He soon understood that this would be the twice-daily routine on weekdays and once only on Saturdays, when work finished at 1pm. His 'tea boy' duty also included recording the daily order, a copy of which he gave to the café each day, and collecting, after the Saturday morning break, all the monies due from the workers, plus a tip, usually one penny, a total weekly tip of around two shillings (10p). This was fantastic, as his starting weekly wage was £1, less health and insurance stamp of 9d (4p) and his pocket money was four shillings (20p). By being tea boy, he was now much better off, an increase of 50%.

A few weeks passed by, during which Dicky was introduced to smoking for real. Like most schoolboys, he'd experimented with the occasional 'scrounged' fag, 'nub ends' and bits of rag, rolled in newspaper, which almost set your mouth on fire. Now, he could afford to buy a packet of ten 'Gold Leaf' cigarettes, costing one shilling and fourpence (7p) and Dicky, like the other youngsters at work, would make one cigarette last for at least three short sessions each working day and have the remaining five to enable him to look big and grown up at the week-end. Got to grow up quickly! A seemingly absolute essential for all kids and encouraged by film stars and popular advertising. Dicky would have no inkling of the fact that three years later, at the age of 17, he would stop smoking in his quest to save and afford the racing bike of his dreams.

He also learnt how to converse in 'back slang', a seemingly incomprehensible way of talking confidentially, by not sounding the first hard phonetic part of any word beginning with a consonant, and adding it on the end of the word with an 'ay' attached.

For example – "otway ooday ouyay inkthay ouyay areay oingday?" means, what do you think you are doing?

Most of the kids at Alfred Davis conversed in this fashion, much to the annoyance of the older workers and a common shout was, "oopidstay odsay!" or "aftday attway!" – Worked it out yet?

Dicky also soon found out that there were two rival gangs. The wood-side, of which he was a conscript, and the wood-wool side, made up of the kids who worked on the production of wool, rendered from all the scrap offcuts etc. and used as packing for the large variety of wooden cases manufactured there. Both gangs were similar in size, seven or eight each in number and hostilities were rarely more serious than 'ambushes', hostage taking and the occasional bout of fisticuffs, fair fist fights. Generally speaking, the use of feet, weapons etc. were not acceptable or practised at the time, the Marquis of Queensbury's rules for boxing, having filtered down to the masses via black and white films and newsreels, being generally accepted.

One lunchtime break, several weeks later, Dicky was filling a sack with wood offcuts lying around in the yard adjacent to the entrance of the wood-wool workshop. When filled and secured with twine or wire, he would hide the sack behind one of the stacks of planks near the rear gates. Just before 'clocking out' at the end of the day, Dicky would lift the sack and drop it over the gate, into the firm's driveway entrance in St Paul's Road, just around the corner from the front entrance in Moseley Road, St Paul's church being on the corner. Dicky would collect his bike from the front, cycle round the back, lift the sack on to the cross-bar and cycle home, steering one handed, the other hand keeping the sack in place. Something you could not do on a bike with low-slung handle-bars. This taking of waste wood wasn't considered stealing, but not encouraged either, so Dicky always contrived to do it 'on the quiet' about once weekly, a useful fuel addition now his Mom wasn't earning a wage.

This particular lunchtime Dicky had been seized by members of the rival gang and taken into their 'territory'. There he was strapped to the long movable saw-bench, used for 'length cutting' planks. One of the 'enemy' then grabbed hold of the big metal handle and started to turn it, thereby causing the bench, and Dicky to traverse towards the stationary circular saw, head first.

From his position Dicky couldn't see the circular saw, but he knew what it was capable of and was feeling distinctly uncomfortable. He refused to show it though, in the sure knowledge they wouldn't really harm him. It was all about scare tactics and he would have done the same if the roles were reversed.

The gang leader, a big 17 year old lad waiting to be called up for war service, thrust his face down about 2 inches from Dicky's and hissed, "think we're just muckin' about, don'cha! Well we ain't, see!"

He motioned with his hand and Dicky moved onward again, but much slower, his eyes wide and straining to see what his head was approaching. He felt something pushing against his mop of frizzy hair then something sharp against his skull.

"No! y'bloody fools, what d'you think y'doin' For chrissake Let me up!"

The gang boss, a malevolent look on his face, leered at Dicky and said, a bit louder, "Any last wish before we cuts you in 'arf?"

He paused, waiting. Dicky was trying to look unconcerned. He knew deep down that they wouldn't hurt him. But he also knew that the slightest pressure on the turning handle would cause him to move forward, head first. What if the kid on the handle suddenly sneezed, or coughed, or slipped? His own fertile imagination wasn't going to get him out of this. It was only making it worse! "Let me up!" he tried to say nonchalently, but it came out like a yelp.

With a demonic wave of his hand, the big kid motioned to wind Dicky back about 6 inches and shouted "Think we're jokin' eh! Start the saw!"

Dicky heard the low hum of the motor and the rasping sound of the saw, as it built up speed until it was almost screaming as loud as Dicky was yelling, when he realised he was being wound forward again. Expecting to feel his head cut through any moment and at the same time not understanding why, as he knew he must have moved forward at least 12 inches, he suddenly realised the gang were all about him, laughing at him whilst they undid the straps, the sound of the saw now slowing down.

Weakly and mightily relieved, Dicky clambered down and looked to see the circular saw still revolving on a cross-cut saw-bench adjacent to the one he had been strapped on. One of the lads was holding up another ordinary hand-saw and, whilst Dicky watched, stuck it in the slot in the saw-bench, where Dicky's head had been.

"You bastards!" shouted Dicky, as the gang made themselves scarce. He was still in a state of near terror, but now quickly realising what a fantastic stunt they'd pulled. When Billy Moore, the foreman, came round the corner and asked him what he was up to, Dicky replied, "nothin', just 'aving a look round" and scarpered.

Billesley Arcadians *and the Parrot!*

Spring had arrived and so had Maurice's birthday. With a self-satisfied smile, he was sitting by the fire smoking a 'Players' cigarette, much to the annoyance of Mrs Blood, who'd known he smoked for some time, but not when she was around. He'd already sent off his application letter volunteering for the Fleet Air Arm and now understood that he'd have to wait until he was 17. He was fed up with his job as a plumbers mate, as was Mrs Blood who had to try and get his clothes, always greasy, stained, and stinking of the muck plumbers used, reasonably clean for the start of the week. He'd got a steady girlfriend too. Seemingly, she didn't mind the smell of tallow.

Dicky, who'd been home for 7 weeks now, was getting fed up with being subordinate to Maurice, who Dicky imagined, delighted in bossing him around. What was more galling was the fact that Maurice could now smoke in the house with impunity, he had got a girlfriend, and he seemed much more than twenty-two months older than Dicky. He was certainly far more knowledgeable regarding films, radio programmes, big showbands and their 'star' singers. He'd also got a 'wind up' record player to play the 78's of jazz and blues he'd bought since starting work two years before.

Maurice was also the solo drummer for Billesley Arcadians, a blue and yellow clad, street marching band of mainly young girls playing 'gazoo' type trumpets, cymbals and triangles and boys playing drums. The band was organised and coached by Joycie Bentley's Dad, with the help of one or two other men. They were led, when playing and marching, by the eldest of the six Bentley daughters, Laurie, who with her mace swinging, throwing and pointing, was a show on her own. As was her younger sister, Evelyn, later on. Laurie's husband 'Bill' was a very good drummer and normally played solo, but he was away in the Royal Navy.

Winter was the time for band practise, held every Friday evening in the hall of Yardley Wood Infant school, at the rear of their row of houses. There, the drummers would stand in one spot whilst the group of 30-40 girls marched and counter marched into different formations, whilst the drummers played. When Harry Bentley was

Billesley Arcadians, taken in 1938

satisfied with the marching and formations, he would order a full-scale workout, complete with drums and 'gazoos' etc. To a kid like Dicky, fresh from the 'farming' country, it was magic, especially when he was invited to join as one of the drummer boys.

With some extra tuition from Maurice, no problem as the drums were only kept next door at the Bentleys, Dicky was soon reasonably capable and able to repeat the various drum tunes satisfactorily. If he wasn't very sure, he wouldn't bang very hard. But, when he was more sure of himself, he'd 'bladder' away like a maniac, that is until, he 'bladdered' his drumstick through a new pigskin right outside the Warstock public house one Sunday morning, where they were putting on a show for the pub drinkers and passers-by, prior to taking the collecting tin round. Harry Bentley, not too pleased and mindful of the watching crowd, contained himself with a whispered "take your drum and sod off 'ome. I'll speak to you later."

Dicky, somewhat chastened and crestfallen, uniformed and carrying the obviously damaged drum, walked the half mile home, alone and grinless.

Each summer there would be carnivals in and around Birmingham, usually held on the sports grounds of the many large manufacturing companies. There would be various sporting competitions, stalls, amusements, shows and the marching band competition, in which up to a dozen or more bands from all over the Midlands would take part. 'Pitmaston Caledonians', 'Yardley Wood Academicals', 'Warwick Diehards', 'Billesley Arcadians' and others. All the bands in turn would demonstrate their individual countermarching and formation displays to their particular music and Billesley Arcadians won many trophies, the judges, maybe convinced by Harry Bentley's favourite and very loud criticism, "sounds like a bleedin' sardine packin' factory!"

This typical 'Brummie' comment not unlike the comment made a few months later, by Maurice on August 17th, when a vociverous baby was born at home, to Dolly Blood, her sixth child. "Sounds like a bleedin' parrot!"

Maurice had exclaimed, waiting with the rest of the kids downstairs, the older ones being aware that 'it was about to happen', as the midwife had visited a couple of times that morning already. Billy Blood, who had been up and down like a yoyo, with tea, hot water etc, came down, his flushed face adorned with a big grin and said, "It's a girl! You can all go up in a minnit an' say 'ello."

The two eldest boys looked at each other, mouths open and momentarily speechless. Nobody had expected a girl. Not after having five boys. You can't play with a girl! It was left to Maurice to put into words what they were thinking. "That's buggered it! We can't play three a side now. We needed a boy to make things even."

Billy blood laughed and said "let me tell you poor sods something! Whoever gets Rita on their side will whack the arse of any other side! She was almost running when she popped out and just listen to her now!"

"Rita! Is that what she's gonna be called?" one of the younger kids exclaimed from his temporary position, one leg already dangling outside the living room open window, a well used route to the garden when their parents were absent. He dropped down the other side of the window, thrust his head back into the room and shouted "can we call the baby Reet?"

A sulk in the apple tree

Maurice, who was as fed up with tidying the garden as Dicky, said, "Fancy a spar Dicky? Like we used to with the gloves Dad bought us?"

"Yeah!! Good idea," responded Dicky, privately thinking, 'great! Now's my chance to get my own back.'

He was fed up with Maurice ordering him about and telling him what to do all the time. 'Who did he think he was anyway?'

"Where's the gloves then 'Moss'?" asked Dicky, keen as mustard. He'd show Maurice a thing or two. Dicky knew he was faster, much quicker on his feet and he knew he would easily perplex Maurice with his rapid fancy footwork, nifty feints, ducks, weaving and straight punching. "Come on then 'Moss', where's the gloves?"

"There ain't no gloves, you daft buggar! They got burnt, full o' slack (coal dust), on the fire years ago. We'll use socks, two pairs each. I bet you haven't even got two pairs."

"I 'ave" Dicky responded and they went off to search under the beds, where socks, odd ones and pairs usually lurked, until Mrs Blood found time to search every nook and corner of the house for clothes casually discarded by any one of the five brothers.

"You've got one of my socks there!" yelped Dicky, as they both emerged from the house. "Where did you find that?"

"On the floor, where else?" replied Maurice, adding, "I see you'e got a pair of Barry's there then."

They both laughed and squared up to each other, gloves raised.

Dicky, showing no concern for Maurice' size, pranced forward extravagantly, the socks flapping and sliding up and down his skinny wrists.

"For Christ's sake! Stop jumping about like an idiot and put some rubber bands around your wrists. There's plenty in the button tin."

After finding the rubber bands and securing the socks, Dicky again advanced towards Maurice. Shuffle, feint, weave, duck, then let go a straight left aimed at Maurice's face. Bang! The hard, sock covered fist landed flush on Dicky's mouth, his own punch failing to reach the target. Dicky staggered, hurt and puzzled.

Maurice was grinning, "copped ya with that one, didn't I?" He was imitating Dicky's earlier prancing around the lawn and shouting "Cm'n then, cm'n!"

He stopped, let go a straight left and right at an imaginary target, at the same time shouting "bang! Bang! I could have knocked you into Bentley's garden with a second punch if I'd 'ave wanted, but I could see you were hurt and amazed. You've forgotten that Dad taught us both an' my arms are longer than your'n."

They sparred on for a few more minutes, Dicky slowly realising that his tactics were not going to work against Maurice's straight left, which always seemed to be in his face. It was no good. Dicky just could not land a decent punch and Maurice was enjoying himself tapping Dicky's face just hard enough to sting and annoy him.

"Sod it! I've 'ad enough o' this game of marlies!" Dicky muttered, pulling off the socks, leaving them where they fell and making his way towards the back door of the house.

"Don't put them away, will ya?" Maurice shouted, picking up the socks as he passed. He gave Dicky a shove in the back and triumphantly announced, "Anytime you fancy your chances shortarse!" grinned and went on his way.

Dicky, mortified, hurt and angry, went up the garden path, climbed up into the apple tree, his favourite place and sat eating an unripe Bramley cooking apple, no big deal for a 14 year old boy. While he chewed he pondered on this new situation. Maurice could beat him. What's more, Maurice was confident of that fact. Sure, Maurice had grown more than Dicky over the last four years and was certainly stronger, due no doubt to the fact that Maurice had left school at 14 years old and had been working as a plumbers mate for over two. The remedy was obvious to Dicky. He had to start growing and he had to acquire more boxing skills. It seemed pretty daft to practice ducking, weaving, feinting etc., if you couldn't land a decent punch on target, especially if that target hit back frequently and too hard for comfort.

Dicky finished the apple, swung from a lower branch for a while, then just hung there by his hands, for as long as he could bear the pain, letting go, seemingly about two seconds before his arms left their sockets. He vaguely wondered why his spine stretching exercises didn't seem to be having any effect, especially as his arms and shoulders ached so. "I'll probably end up a shortarse with very long arms!" he muttered to himself and with an "oh! Sod it! wandered back towards the house.

A few weeks later, Maurice, who had volunteered for the navy at the age of 16 years, was called up for basic training and was soon on his way. His subordinate, ordinary seaman Dicky Blood, depending on the game of the day, was now in charge. Only during the absence of his parents though.

A New Job

Dicky, whilst recovering from a broken arm sustained through larking about on the stacks of timber at Alfred Davis, had met Dennis, a lad of similar age, at the Moseley Road swimming baths.

Dennis worked for a small firm that made wall clocks. The company was in Balsall Heath and was about one mile from Alfred Davis's, where Dicky worked. According to Dennis, the company, Eaves and Co. of Charles Henry Street, needed another boy as one of the present staff had been called up for the Army.

It really was an amazing period. Because of the need for more production of just about everything to do with war and obviously the need for, more than normal, manpower, or should that be woman power, every company, large and small, had to not only make do, but produce more, without the traditional workforce of 18-40year old men. They were needed elsewhere, millions of them, in all the forces in direct conflict on several fronts, land, sea and air as well as coalmines.

It would prove to be a cultural, social and economical shock to returning servicemen when they discovered the 'little woman' at home could graft and handle complex machinery. Not only that, the many girls and young women who volunteered for any one of the Armed Services, proved they were equal to the many difficult tasks given them and this historic subject has been well researched and documented by several authors since.

Eaves and Co, like all other companies, depended on older, or unfit for war service, men and boys under the age of 17 and a half, and women. They had a full order book, consisting mainly of wall clocks for all the Post Office shops throughout the UK and a few 'specials' made to order, such as granddaughter clocks, which were scaled down half sized grandfather clocks. They needed a boy. Dicky turned up with Dennis and he was offered the job at seven shillings a week more than his present job. What's more, he was promised he'd have the opportunity to learn some skills.

Dicky happily accepted and went into Alfred Davis's the following Monday, his first day back after six weeks away on 'mandatory sick pay', about one third of normal earnings, different if you are an office worker or other 'white collar staff' who got 'full pay'. As soon as Billy Moore, the foreman, appeared in the workshop on his normal morning round, Dicky gleefully shouted across the workshop "eh! Bill! I wanna give a weeks notice."

Billy Moore looked at him, said he was going to sack him that week anyway and that was that. A kid wasn't going to put one across Billy Moore, no way.

Dicky's first job, on his first day at Eaves & Co, would never be forgotten. He was immediately responsible for the glue. Each morning he would have to put the glue pot on the gas ring and stir it until the contents were hot and runny. He would also have to 'top up' the pot as required, with fresh lumps of hard glasslike fish glue and stir them in. The glue was used to stick together the ready-cut wooden assemblies, which formed the clock housings. When partially set, panel pins and screws were used to permanently secure them.

After a couple of days getting used to the glue routine Dicky was 'lent' a small hammer and showed how to correctly assemble the clock housings around the 'jig' provided, after first applying the glue, then a few strategically placed panel pins. He'd do ten assemblies in this fashion, carefully placing them on the workbench so that he could add the final fixing screws in the order that they were assembled. Ten would take about one hour to assemble and fix, after which, Dicky would apply woodstain, and then stack them.

Whilst they were drying in the warmest part of the workshop, Dicky would repeat the process with another ten assemblies and stack alongside the first and so on. As the stacks dried, Dicky would then carry the housings, five at a time, upstairs to the French polishing department, one large room occupied by clean flat benches and Alice, the French polisher, a very small middle-aged woman, slim, of pale complexion and grey streaked black hair tied back in a bun. On the end bench there would be 'finished', smoothly glistening, housings, resting on narrow wooden strips laid on top of sheets of newspaper. In front of Alice would be receptacles containing her tools of trade, fine sandpaper, brushes, and small pieces of felt, French polish and spirits. Alice was stone deaf beyond any medical expertise at the time. Amazingly, she was the mother of ten children and the favourite joke related to all newcomers, when meeting Alice, was about her husband bellowing in Alice's ear, when in bed, "d'you want to go to sleep or what?" Alice, not hearing properly, would reply "what?" Grown ups would immediately 'get the joke'. Dicky, rapidly learning 'workshop floor' facts of life, thought he did.

The weeks went by and Dicky had the opportunity, as promised, to try his hand at various operations. The small firm had two main departments, apart from Alice's shop and the office, both on the top floor of the old, brick built, three story building. The second floor comprised the woodworking department, in which three men, plus Dicky and Dennis worked. The cellar basement contained the 'brass' section, where the incoming rolls of different size brass strip were cut into required lengths, shaped into various diameter hoops and brazed, 'turned' on revolving wooden chucks, driven via descending leather belts, by one long overhead shaft, powered by an electric motor. The finished products were called 'bezels' and secured the glass to the clock face. This lower floor never saw daylight and was lit by three strategically placed electric lights. Through an open doorway at one end was the toilet, a basic urinal and two cubicles, again with no doors. There was no light and no wash basin, which in that unenlightened time didn't seem very unusual, but, from a 'Gaffer's' point of view, quite acceptable. Dicky never found out where Mr Eaves and Alice 'went', but it was a fact that Dicky and the rest of the dozen or so male workers, didn't use the toilet unless it was desperate, especially as the river Rea ran alongside and rats were regularly seen in the basement. Lovely!

The Race

It was 'dinner' time and Dicky and some of his work colleagues were
enjoying a sit outside in the warm sun of mid September. Wally, the
eldest worker at about 35 years and unfit for war service, was
holding forth about the yearly competition for the inter-departmental
cup, a small pewter two handled cup that was 'battled' for every
year, usually on a dartboard.

"I reckon we ought to 'ave a bike race for a change. All the kids 'ere
'ave got bikes, so we can 'ave two kids from each department, seein'
as we've only got two kids on our side."

Dicky and Dennis thought it was a great idea, as did seventeen year
old Ron from the 'brass' side. Sixteen year old Ray, one of the 'brass'
side workers, was voted in as Ron's partner, mainly because Ray had
a nice looking lightweight bike.

The race would take place the following day at 1.30pm, over a course
that took in the three streets that made a triangular one mile route
back to the start outside the entrance to the company premises. It was
decided that three laps would be enough as the first street, Vaughan
St. South, was the longest and all uphill, the second street, which they
would turn left into, was much shorter and downhill, but had
tramlines to contend with, and the last street, Charles Henry St.,
which they again turned left into, was long and flat. Wally, setting
himself up as the expert, estimated that it would take the winner
about 20 minutes and the stragglers half an hour to finish.

The following day was again dry and just about everyone at Faves &
Co were looking forward to dinner time. Wally, during the morning
break, had announced he was 'making a book' on the race and
declared the 'odds'. The clear favourite was Ron, because he was the
oldest and had got a decent looking bike with low handlebars and
gears. The second favourite was Ray, because he was the second
oldest and had also got a decent looking lightweight bike, with
'straight bar' handlebars. The third favourite was Dennis, because he
was a few months older and a bit bigger than Dicky. His bike also

looked sportier than Dicky's standard roadster. The rank outsider with no chance at all was Dicky, because he was the youngest, the smallest and he'd got the worst and heaviest looking bike.

The odds were:

> Ron - Evens
> Ray - 2 to 1
> Dennis - 5 to 1
> Dicky - 10 to 1

Most of the money, only tanners (2.5p) really, went on Ron. Dennis backed himself with 6d(2.5). No one, not even Ray, backed Ray and only two people backed Dicky, Alice, who took a chance with 6d and Dicky, who also risked 6d. Dicky thought Wally had got it all wrong and hadn't taken into account Dicky's 10 mile round journey every day, by far much longer than anyone else. He also didn't know that Dicky was barmy about racing and competition and would strive almost every night to beat his own 'best time', when going home.

The following morning, during tea break, Dicky spent the time in the 'bike room' removing the mudguards, saddlebag, lamps and lamp brackets in an effort to make his bike look like a 'Tour de France' racing bike. Of course it didn't, but it was a bit lighter and when he wheeled it out at lunchtime, Wally hollered "eh! wot's this then. This ain't your usual bike. Wot's the game y'little bleeder?"

Dicky assured him that it was the same bike less a few bits and pieces and after a quick inspection Wally agreed saying, "won't make much of a difference, about 20 yards, I reckon." Wally, being a 'greyhound' man and a bit of an expert on racing 'form' was satisfied and said the betting odds remained unchanged.

At 1.30pm, the four competitors lined up behind the chalked start and finish line and were given the '1,2,3 and off' by Mr Eaves, who'd come down from his office to watch the fun. Ron immediately pedalled off in the lead closely followed by Dicky, head down, and forearms flat against the handlebars, legs furiously pumping. Dennis was close behind Dicky and Ray just couldn't keep up from the start and was soon far behind.

The second lap was much like the first. Ron, head down, pedalling hard and using his gears as necessary. Dicky, so close behind that their wheels were almost touching, Dennis was way back and Ray only completed one lap and gave up.

Going up the hill on the third lap, Dicky was wondering if he'd have enough strength to get past Ron and when to try. However, his mind was made up for him. Furiously pedalling, they both turned into the shorter downhill street with the tramlines. Part way down was a van parked on their side of the road, which wasn't there the other times they'd raced by. They both pulled out, one after the other, but one of Ron's narrower wheels momentarily went into one of the tramlines, slowing him briefly, but sufficiently enough, to allow Dicky to get past on the inside. With a tremendous feeling of exultancy, Dicky swept by Ron, took the left turn at speed into the last street and, head down, pedalled as fast as his legs would go towards the finish about 600 yards away. Ron, only momentarily delayed, was immediately, and to Dicky's dismay, already on his tail and enjoying the 'vacuum' pulls, just as Dicky had for the first two laps.

Oblivious to the roaring crowd of spectators lining the route, 'Wilson' (of the Wizard), the mystery superhuman athlete who had so often come to England's aid during the last 10 years or so, realised that Maes, the Belgian long distance champion and winner of the Tour de France just before Germany invaded, had tricked him into taking the lead and was now just 'sitting in' a few feet behind his rear wheel. 'Wilson' knew that the Belgian would wait until about 150 yards from the finish, then rapidly close up and at the last moment, swing out and using his gained extra velocity, overtake 'Wilson' and win. Well, that would be the Belgian champion's plan.

'Wilson' had other ideas though. Despite his own racing bike being damaged beyond repair in the 'unfortunate accident' at 80 miles with the Belgian support vehicle which, suddenly and unexplainably, reversed across the road into Wilson, who luckily managed to leap clear, and having to make do with the only other bike available, borrowed off the local postman, 'Wilson's well known tenacity and almost superhuman strength had enabled him stay with the Belgian as the two of them, having left the rest of the large international field far behind, battled it out over the remaining few miles of the 100 mile race. With about one hundred yards to go to the finish, Maes pulled out to make his challenge and almost side-by-side they raced for the line.

Both cyclists, heads down, bodies arched, legs pumping, the veins on their temples, necks and bulging muscles standing out like purple rivulets, hurtled towards the finish outside Buckingham Palace, where Royalty, officialdom and the Press and Pathe Gazette photographers were gathered.

Dicky, lungs on fire, legs rapidly weakening, could see out of the corner of his right eye, the front wheel of Ron's bike slowly creeping closer. He couldn't lose now. Mentally screaming at his legs to go faster and aware that Ron must be feeling exactly the same, Dicky, almost sobbing with the effort, and Ron raced over the line almost together. Both riders just stopped pedalling and tried to keep some sort of control of their bikes with bodies and limbs completely devoid of energy and strength. They slowly wheeled round, almost fell off and slumped against the wall in a heap, gasping for breath and probably praying for the pain to go away.

"Who won?" gasped Ron.

"Dicky, by about three inches, according to Mr Eaves," replied Wally, himself out of breath and red-faced.

"I reckon it was closer, but Dicky was the winner, no doubt about that. Good race mind! Another 20 yards an' it might 'ave bin different."

Ron nodded at Dicky and still breathing hard said "you wouldn't give up, y' little bugger!"

"Neither would you!" replied Dicky, squeezing the words from his burning lungs.

Wally, as bookmaker, lost, but had the good grace to admit his 'form' forecasting was 'up the creek'. Alice was very happy and so was Dicky.

First Girlfriend

It was September 1944 and Dicky had acquired a girlfriend named Mary. She was 13 years old and still at school. A small girl, with a pretty face that belied her age and a winsome way about her, she had several 'suitors', her last regular boyfriend being Johnny Tipper, a lad the same age as Dicky and both unaware that their paths would cross several times as adversaries in the years ahead.

What Mary saw in Dicky, he didn't know or care. He just felt so lucky that she wanted to be with him. Every weekend and a couple of times in the week, they would be together. Cinema, swimming, walks and most evenings sitting in the same lounge chair, in the window alcove, behind the curtains in the living room of the house owned by her father, Mr Marsh and her stepmother. Also living there were her gorgeous elder sister Joan and Robert, her baby son, her husband being away in the Navy. Another baby, James, he being the son of Mr Marsh and Mary's stepmother, Mary's young cousin Pat and her parents. And the head of the family, Granny Marsh, a timeworn wrinkled old lady with a quick tongue, a vast store of 'home truths' and remedies and had for many years, been a 'wet' nurse. All of these lived, seemingly quite happily, in a 3 bed roomed council house in Ravenshill Road, just round the corner from where Dicky lived in School Road.

Dicky, being the second of six children, easily 'fitted in' this household and was made welcome there. When Bob, Joan's husband, came home on his first leave from many months away at sea, Dicky was invited to the party and had his first taste of port wine mixed with lemonade. He liked it.

What Dicky didn't like so much was the 'hanger on' pal of Mary's that often turned up and accompanied them, much to Dicky's annoyance.

"He's alright" Mary would say, " I've known him for ages, but I've never wanted him as a boyfriend."

'Teddy', the boy in question, was a few months older than Dicky and obviously thought this gave him the right to advise on anything and everything.

One day, whilst out walking with Mary and 'Teddy' in close attendance, Dicky recognised one of a pair of youths walking towards them. It was Reg Gutteridge, the kid he'd fought with, before the 'scrap' with Reggie Kettle four years before. The youth with him was bigger and looked a couple of years older. As they got closer, Gutteridge muttered something to his pal, who immediately grabbed Dicky and twisted his arm up his back.

"'Old 'im while I give 'im one" Gutteridge chortled and advanced, fist drawn back.

He swung the punch at Dicky who ducked beneath it shouting, "missed! Try again!"

Gutteridge's punch hit his pal who promptly let go of Dicky and soon the protagonists were rolling around on the grassy street verge, trying to land a 'goodun', with Mary hopping all over the place on one foot, in her attempts to hit Gutteridge with her shoe.

A couple of workers from the bus depot across the road, put a stop to the 'scrap' with the issue undecided and both boys hurling threats about the next time they met.

Afterwards, whilst walking home, Mary wanted to know what the fight was all about and Dicky explained, describing that day four years previously, when he'd had three 'scraps' in about 20 minutes, including the one with Gutteridge.

"I've never had a fight," said Teddy, listening for a change.

"Well stick with me" replied Dicky. "I just can't seem to avoid them." Dicky and Mary never saw Teddy again. Wasn't that a bloody shame!

Make Your Mind Up

1945

It was now well into winter. Christmas had passed by, during which Dicky had taken young Duggie round to Mary's place for a family Christmas party where small presents were exchanged, games were played and Pat told Mary she'd like Duggie for a sweetheart.

On learning of this exciting news, eleven-year-old Duggie said, "I don't want a sweetheart. They take up too much time. I'd rather play football and cricket."

His reply, so definite, clear and unarguable, insinuated itself into Dicky's brain and caused him, over the next few weeks, to consider his own position. He thought he loved Mary and she was always saying she loved him and writing him little love notes. He certainly didn't want to go out with any other girl and enjoyed every moment he spent with 'his girl', but, he was still a few weeks short of his 15th birthday and, as his older brother Maurice kept telling him, too young to settle down with one 'bint'. He resolved to see less of Mary and concentrate on new ventures.

During the next few weeks Dicky and Mary joined The Woodcraft Folk, a youth club for under 17's. As the name of the club implied, it was a social club, where for two hours a week, the kids, under the supervision of an adult Leader, would play games, learn about things relating to the UK fauna and flora and go camping. The kids were all given animal names, Dicky's being 'Puma', and each evening would consist of 1 hour listening to a 'talk' about wildlife and 1 hour playing team games. It was different, good fun and somewhere to go other than Mary's house for a change, as English winters were notoriously unfriendly to evening strollers, especially if there was no moon about, the wartime blackout still being in force.

Spring came, and so did a new outfit for Mary, who was leaving school at the end of term. Complete with new shoes and a hairdo, she paraded and twirled in front of Dicky. Her beaming face, rarely miserable anyway, showed signs of a discreet make-up by her sister Joan. She was stunningly beautiful, looked at least two years older than 14 and teased Dicky unmercifully.

"I don't think we ought to wait until I'm 15 before we get engaged," She said, snuggling up to him. "I think we ought to get engaged a lot sooner, get married soon after, and have a baby like Robert."

Dicky didn't know what to say. He liked the idea, but Crikey! Not yet. He knew raising a family was all important to Mary, maybe because there were two babies in the house, which Dicky knew she enjoyed looking after. She certainly wasn't interested in a career, her immediate aim when leaving school, was to be a shop assistant. He also knew that they hadn't talked with conviction about engagement, marriage or kids, although as far as he was concerned, it was a nice thought but in about 8-10 years time. Mary kissed him, hugged him and jumped up laughing, "don't look so worried. I didn't mean it." She then put on her serious face, stepped closer, looked up into Dicky's eyes and said "well not yet." Dicky was perplexed, doubly so.

He was fully aware of the fact that his own 'career' wasn't 'up to much'. He could already see the scope for improvement just wasn't there at his present job and he'd also realised that he didn't want to be a carpenter.

"An apprenticeship! That's what you want," said his Dad and for several weeks now they'd been scanning the papers for something suitable.

Meanwhile, another pal he'd met at the swimming baths had introduced Dicky to the BSA Boxing Club, one of the very few sporting clubs of any sort in Birmingham and part of The Birmingham Small Arms Group, Gun makers and Machine Tool manufacturers.

Dicky's first visit to the club, at the side of the BSA sports ground, was exhilarating. The sounds and spectacle of so many men and youths training, sparring, skipping, shadow boxing and exercising. The smell of sweat and embrocation, the sound of pain, grunts, the slap of leather and skipping ropes, the clanging of the bell and clatter of the sponge bucket. It was all new and wonderful and Dicky decided there and then he wanted to be a boxer. He was given a skipping rope, shown how to skip to improve limb co-ordination, put through some exercises with a group of other youngsters, then taken out in a group running round the streets of Sparkbrook and Small

Heath, in the charge of an ex-army physical training instructor and boxer. He would sing his 'mantra' as they ran,

"No booze and no fags.
No girls and no slags.
No sin, if you wanna win.
The more you train, the more you gain."

This continued for several weeks and when Dicky enquired about having a go in the ring, he was told not to be in a hurry, there was plenty of time to 'get yer nose bust'! So the exercises, skipping and running continued, with Dicky, now wondering "ow the 'ell' he was ever going to become a boxer.

It was about this time that Dicky heard that BSA Tools, the Machine Tool side of BSA, required boys to complete five-year apprenticeships, commencing at the age of 16.

He applied, sat the relevant tests and was accepted on the understanding that he would go to night school and improve his educational standard, which, he'd already found out, was poor. So poor in fact, that he didn't even understand Duggie's homework and he was only 12 years old, but had been back at Yardley Wood school for some time now. On that basis, Dicky started his employment with BSA Tools, Montgomery St, Sparkbrook, a couple of weeks later, working in a department that stamped the make and size on a variety of drills, reamers etc. His formal apprenticeship training to start later, on his 16th birthday in February 1946.

Realising his long-term commitment to education and training and his new found interest in boxing, Dicky went to see Mary's sister Joan, who now was living in one of the new Prefabs in School Road, not far from Dicky's house. He explained as best he could that he was going to finish with Mary completely and why. He hoped Joan would understand and said he wasn't going to get 'involved' with another girl again until he was 19 or 20, 'really grown up' and with more idea of his future.

Joan listened, understood, and when Dicky 'grasped the nettle' and told Mary of his plans, was able to offer some sisterly comfort. Meanwhile Dicky, himself feeling pretty miserable, got on with the rest of his quite turbulent life.

Victory in Europe (VE Day)

May 8th 1945

Everyone knew the war was in its final stages. All reports on the wireless, in the newspapers and visibly supported by 'Pathe News' at the cinemas, made this clear.

Despite this, when the announcement was finally made on the radio, the whole population went barmy. At last, after 5 years of carnage, death, despair and misery, it was all over. People could start to live again and plan for the future. Dicky, like all the other kids in the street, carried things back and forth helping the adults set up tables and chairs for the street party later that day. Bunting, last used for the Coronation in 1937, was re-discovered in cupboards, attics and sheds, also Union Jacks. The only piano in that part of the street was being played by its owner, Mrs Left, in support of the 'wind-up' gramophone, playing just about any record found. Even the hymn 'Abide with me' was played, creating a temporary, solemn, tearful pause in memory of those who had been killed, including Mrs Left's husband, George, an upper gunner in a Lancaster bomber that failed to return. Despite the shortages and rationing, store cupboards 'gave up' various saved 'goodies' for the occasion. There were parties everywhere and hundreds of hastily assembled bonfires lit up the night sky of Birmingham and the rest of the country.

The blackout was finished, over and done with and Vera Lynn would sing to the people 'When the lights go on again'. A few days later there was a mass march past in the centre of Birmingham of all the various armed services, the civil services, police, British legion, Boys Brigade, scouts and guides, carnival street marching bands and many others. Billesley Arcadians, including 'drummer boy' Dicky, marched along with the rest of them through the city centre and crowds of ordinary Birmingham folk, shouting, waving, cheering and clapping. Each and every one determined to express their relief and delight that at last, it was all over.

The assembly time for this monumental march past involving thousands was 7pm. The fact that the march started at 7pm, was

VE Day Celebrations 1945–Sandmere Road, Yardley Wood, Birmingham

down to the excellent bus services that carried everyone, marchers and crowds, from all the outlying districts of 'Brum'. Could that be achieved today? Unfortunately for many, including Billesley Arcadians, the last bus from the city centre to the outskirts of the city was at 10pm and still would be for many years after. The Arcadians, including many youngsters below the age of 11 years, and a few veterans of the First World War, were obliged to walk the five miles home to Yardley Wood. This they did in orderly fashion, to the single beat of one drum, each of the drummers taking a turn as required. It didn't matter. Everyone was tired, but it seemed that everyone knew and felt, it was a definitive moment in time.

BSA Tools

1945

The factory in Montgomery Street was large and occupied several acres of land, bordered on one side by a canal and by Montgomery St, on the other. Several hundred people, including 30 or more apprentices, were employed there in the manufacture of small tools. Most of the machinery was old and belt driven, but new machinery was in evidence, much of it American.

Like most wartime factories, the majority of employees were women, the rest being older skilled men, a few 'unfit for war duties' men, young boys and girls, and of course, the apprentices, about 30 of them, all boys. Who'd ever heard of girls going into that dirty engineering!!

There was a works canteen, where you could get a dinner and pudding for 6d(2.5p), which also doubled as a social club for the workers. Nothing fancy, just folding chairs and tables, a small raised 'stage' for the 'resident' band of amateur musicians, probably employees, on piano, trumpet, saxophone and drums. On a 'special occasion' night, a semi-professional band would be hired, six or seven musicians, plus a singer who'd 'knock you dead' with her glamour and voice. Amateur or professional, the small available space for dancing would be full. There would also be a drinks bar or some other satisfactory arrangement for getting a drink.

To the modern pleasure seeker, these facilities would seem amateurish, cheap and a place to avoid. But in that era of war, uncertainty, rationing, wholesale worldwide slaughter of military forces and innocent people, it was an escape for a few wonderful, stress free, hours of entertainment and social activity. That is, until the sirens blasted out.

The first morning passed by quickly for Dicky as Jim, the section leader, explained what would be expected of him and introduced him to the small staff of four, two middle-aged men labourers and two women on 'roll' presses. Already aware of the existence of the canteen, Dicky, for the first time in his short working life, didn't take sandwiches to work. Told where the canteen was by one of his new workmates, one of the two women on the small 'roll marking' section, he made his way to the main gangway, along which the workers would be going to lunch, only to be almost flattened by the front runners leading the 300 or so workers making their hurried way to dinner. After the first wave had passed, Dicky managed to jump in and smartly trot with the flow, the last 200 yards or so, only to find he was about 50th in the already formed queue at the canteen servery. Although he was served within about 10 minutes, Dicky resolved to be in the forefront of the first wave the very next day, and he was, as were most of the apprentices.

"You can shift a bit" said one of the other lads the following day as Dicky, with his dinner and pudding, always served together, sat down with the crowd he'd ran with.

Dicky grinned and said, "It's me second day 'ere. Yesterday I was back there with that lot just coming through the door."

"Ar! It don't tek long to get the message," replied the other lad.

They walked back together, the other lad describing the functions of each section as they passed by. His name was Dennis Griffiths, he'd been at BSA Tools almost a year and would be starting the first year of his ONC (Ordinary National Certificate) in September.

Dicky was obliged to tell Dennis, that the Apprentice Supervisor, Mr Davis, had suggested that Dicky do the City and Guilds course, after doing 1st and 2nd preliminary course, whatever that was. Mr Davis explained, that because of his lack of schooling whilst being evacuated, Dicky was three years behind, just like thousands of other evacuees. Not that Dicky realised the significance of that fact then. But he would, when three years later, he found himself at the age of 18, doing the 1st year of the City and Guilds five-year course, with 16year olds.

As the weeks passed by, Dicky got to know most of the other apprentices and became familiar with most of the 'games' they played, usually immediately after dinner. One of the favourite games, for which there were only two rules, only one hammer in one hand and always to face the action, was to place a bit of food under one of the upturned empty work tins, one end of which was raised a few inches off the floor by a piece of wood attached to a long piece of string, the other end of which was firmly held by one of the apprentices.

The lights, necessary at that gloomy end of the factory, were then turned off and the apprentices in the game, usually seven or eight, would quietly sit on the benches watching the work tin closely in the, now very dim light. Almost without fail, within minutes, one or more rats would emerge from under the benches, where presumably they lived, being easily accessible to the canal which ran alongside the factory. Silent, hardly breathing, the watchers would wait until one of the rats, they didn't want more, went fully under the tin. Then the string would be pulled, the lights would go on and the 'hunters' would gather around the work tin at a distance of about 7-8 feet, each armed with one hammer. At a given signal, each of the 'hunters' would crouch and start to hammer the wooden factory floor. After about 20 seconds of 'drumming', the box would suddenly be lifted, by yanking on another long string attached to one of the work tin handles and thrown over a convenient beam. The glare of sudden light and the steady beat of the hammers would momentarily 'stay' the rodent, but not for long.

Sometimes the rat, often as big as 15" long, would take off in one direction in a series of leaps, squealing at the same time in its terror and determination to escape. Sometimes a rat would make tentative moves in various directions before suddenly 'going for it' and sometimes the rat would immediately rush out the moment the tin was lifted enough to allow it to.

As regards the waiting drumming 'hunters' one thing was absolutely certain. Each of their tight little sphincters would be working overtime as they manically increased their drumming at the slightest indication that the rat was coming their way. And when it was suddenly clear which way it was going to charge, or leap, at frightening speed, the high pitched terrified 'mewing' of the boy barring it's way, combined with his frenetic thrashing about with his hammer, at the same time desperately trying to keep both feet off the ground, effected such a high degree of excitement that, quite often, more than one sphincter 'gave way'.

Victory in Japan

1945

The war now ended, everyone thought that rationing would end as well. But it didn't and wouldn't for many years. Dicky, just like every other kid, soon got used to that fact and just got on with life. Now much better anyway, without the black-out restrictions. There was a new mood in the air, even the kids noticed it. Adults were talking about change all the time. Posters were appearing everywhere about a new government. Arguments, sometimes quite aggressive, would spring up out of nowhere. Even amongst kids taking their parent's side in their political choice for the coming elections.

Dicky's parents held meetings in their front room for the local Labour Party. His Dad, short as he was, always appeared to be in the forefront of arguments in The Haven public house, just down the road. "Somebody will kill the argumentative little sod one of these days," Mrs Blood would say on more than one occasion.

Billy Blood would come home flushed with temper, but it never lasted long. After a few minutes sounding off about everything he didn't agree with that day, he'd dismiss it with a good old Anglo Saxon word or three, grin and forget it. He was very, very good at that.

Meanwhile, Dicky was taking some stock of his own life. He was going to commit himself to an engineering apprenticeship until he was 21. He would be going to Technical College, one day a week, for that duration. He would also be attending night school 3 nights weekly to try and catch up with his standard of education. All that was sorted. He was finding it more difficult to save money, simply because the cinema, swimming baths, youth club and boxing club took the bulk of his 5 shillings pocket money. The rest always went on his sweet ration and the odd cake from the bakers shop in Gooch Street.

He wondered how he would get on. Would he ever get THE RACING BIKE? Would he ever become a racing champion? Would he travel round the world, like his Dad had done in the Royal Navy, and now his brother Maurice was hoping to do. Would he become a boxer? Would he ever be able to reach the top of the doorway without jumping?

Yoxall Colloquial Dialect - 1940's

anna or inna	–	have'nt or ain't
munna	–	must'nt
maun	–	must
dunna	–	don't
canna	–	can't
shanna	–	shan't
thrape	–	thrash or flog
showders	–	shoulders
owd	–	old
blitherin	–	moaning
fate	–	feet or fight
rate	–	right
hoost	–	hoarse cough
cowd	–	cold
gorra	–	got
wane	–	we have
weem	–	we are
youm	–	you are
ar	–	our
hadna	–	hadn't
wom	–	home
skooil	–	school
berra	–	betta
sustiffikit	–	certificate
wi	–	with
way	–	we
mornin	–	morning
nate	–	night
didna	–	didn't
weer	–	where
niver	–	never
sate	–	sight
afore	–	before
sowd	–	sold

fowertane	–	fourteen
woth	–	worth
nay	–	no
aye	–	yes
yersen	–	yourself
tomorrer	–	tomorrow
tonate	–	tonight
'aporth	–	halfpennyworth
frit	–	frightened
fost or fust	–	first
brek, brok	–	break, broke
waiter or watter	–	water
corves	–	calves
ship	–	sheep

Dicky Blood's Back Slang

(1) (ickyday ud'sblay akbay angslay)
A 'spoken only' slang, whereby the first consonant part of any word is not sounded but added on to the end of the word with an 'ay' on the end.

For example:

    Udgay means _ _ _ _ _ good
    Adbay _ _ _ _ _ _ _ _ bad
    Eenbay _ _ _ _ _ _ _ _ been
    Oonsay _ _ _ _ _ _ _ soon
    Ichray _ _ _ _ _ _ _ _ rich
    Uitfray _ _ _ _ _ _ _ _ fruit
    Interpray _ _ _ _ _ _ printer
    Antslay _ _ _ _ _ _ _ slant
    Umdray _ _ _ _ _ _ _ drum
    Ermanyjay _ _ _ _ _ _ Germany
    Anksyay _ _ _ _ _ _ _ Yanks
    Ootsbay _ _ _ _ _ _ _ boots
    Appleay _ _ _ _ _ _ _ apple
    Iddlemay _ _ _ _ _ _ _ middle
    Elefonetay _ _ _ _ _ _ telephone

The only place I heard and spoke this 'back slang' was at Alfred Davis, Packing Case makers, Moseley Road, Birmingham, where I was employed for six months in 1944. See story 'Tea Boy'

None of the adult employees used it and I do not know where it originated.

To my knowledge, it was only used phonetically.

Little Known Facts of World War Two

1. *'GERMANY & BRITAIN,* agree not to bomb civilians 3rd September 1939

2. *'DESPERATE TIMES'*, Caused Britain to create a secret network of guerrilla forces, all sworn to secrecy and equipped and trained separately.
See amazing film footage on *www.century20war.co.uk/page4.html*

3. *FIRST OPERATION BY ROYAL AIR FORCE* was on night of 3/4th September 1939, the first night of the war, when Whitley bombers dropped, not bombs but, leaflets over enemy territory.
Ref; www.raf.mod.uk/bombercommand/diary

4. *'REGARDLESS OF COST'.* Yes! That was the order given to the many squadrons of Bristol Blenheim Fighter/Bombers raiding enemy airfields, ports and shipping in August/September 1940. *THE COST* was **147 planes** and **400 young airmen** in just a few weeks. 'The Bristol Blenheim' by Graham Warner (Crecy Publishing)

5. *THE BRISTOL BLENHEIM* was the first plane in the world to be fitted with Radar. Also first plane to sink a German Uboat and first plane to sink a Japanese submarine
Ref; www.aviationclassics.org.uk/blenheim

6. *FIRST DECORATIONS OF WAR* were DFC's to Blenheim pilots F/lt Doran and F/o McPhearson.
Ref; as above

7. *'ROYAL OAK'* The British battleship was sunk by a German Uboat in the 6th week of the war. 833 officers and men perished. Suddenly and tragically, a lot of families knew there was a war on.
Ref; Mike Kemble website

8. 'PHONY AIRCRAFT', were made very cheaply by the British Cinema Industry in 1939. Lightweight, mobile and easily assembled on site, these dummy aircraft were widely deployed on airfields throughout the UK. For further information on Great Britain's Deception Campaign see
http://history.acusd.edu/gen/ww2Timeline/britain.html

9. FOOD, NUTRITION & RATIONING February 1st 1940 Professor J C Drummand was appointed Scientific Advisor to the Ministry of Food. He stressed the importance of high nutritive value bread, oatmeal, green vegetables, cheese and that children up to the age of 15 and expectant mothers should be supplied with at least one pint of milk per day. Obesity was impossible on wartime rations!. *'The Englishman's Food' by J C Drummand and Anne Wilbraham.*

10. DUNKIRK EVACUATION May 1940. The youngest veteran of 'Operation Dynamo' was 14yr old Albert Barnes from Dagenham, who was teaboy on a Thames tug. His boat, *Sun X11*, was called straight off a job, into action, and only returned home 14 days later, having carried out a daring series of rescues. Albert's mother, bursting with pride, showed off his socks to their neighbours. They were so stiff with dirt that they stood up on their own like a pair of wellingtons. But they'd seen action in Dunkirk!

11. 'THE WOODEN AIRCRAFT' 25th November 1940. First flight of De Havilland Mosquito, built mainly of wood. It became one of the most successful aircraft of WW2 as a bomber/fighter, but wasn't very good in Far East because heat affected the wooden structure.
Ref; http://members.lycos.co.uk/mkemble/mosquito.html

12. 'AMAZING FLIGHT' An RAF bomber, Halifax 111 MZ465 after an attack on Saarbrucken, had nine feet of it's nose chopped off when it collided with another bomber over the target. The plane dived 1500 feet after the collision, the pilot struggling to regain control. He managed this and brought the plane up to 11,000 feet again. At this height it stalled, but he managed to keep it at 7000 feet and fly home despite having only three instruments working. No intercom, no compass, no ASI, no radio. Some of the skin on the aircraft nose was bent round to give some protection against the wind whistling through the fuselage, but the captain, Flying Officer A L Wilson and the rest of the crew were frozen as they struggled to keep the aircraft flying. The navigator and the bomb-aimer, neither of whom were wearing parachutes, had fallen out of the aircraft when it collided and were killed.

The 4 engines continued to function perfectly, despite the propellers being damaged, probably by bits of wreckage from the fuselage and the plane and the rest of the crew made it safely home.
Ref; www.raf.mod.uk/bombercommand/squadrons/h51.html

13. 'LANCASTER BOMBER' 9th January 1941. First flight of Avro Lancaster, most successful British Bomber which was powered by 4 Rolls Royce Merlin engines.
Ref; www.raf.mod.uk/bombercommand/aircraft/lancaster.html

14. 'THE SPITFIRE' fighter plane cost £5,000 each and 20,334 were produced
Ref; www.aviationclassics.org.uk

15. 'WARTIME RATIONING', started in 1941, finished in *1954*

16. 'HAPPY BIRTHDAY TO YOU' On Hitler's birthday, Germany celebrated by dropping 1000 tons of bombs on London.

17. 'MANY RETURNS OF THE DAY!' Over 600,000 tons of bombs were eventually dropped on Germany

18. 'WINSTON CHURCHILL' 17th January 1942, was nearly shot down by the enemy and then his own airforce. During a return trip from the USA, his flying boat veered off course and came close to German anti-aircraft guns in France. After this error was noticed and corrected, his aircraft then appeared to British radar operators to be an enemy bomber. Six RAF fighters were scrambled to shoot his plane down, but fortunately, they failed to find him.
Ref; www.stokesey.demon.co.ukwwii/trivia

19. *'LEMONADE FACTORY'* in North Shields hit by German bomb, causing 3 storey factory to collapse on to the basement , killing 102 occupants including 36 children under the age of 16.

20. *'18,000 TONS OF BOMBS'* were dropped on England during 8 months of 'The Blitz'. Those killed included 18,629 men, 16,201 women and 5,028 children.

21. *'AFTER THE BLITZ'*, London contributed over 2 million cubic tons of rubble as hard core for new runways construction at airfields in the UK, including a regular service of 6 trains daily to East Anglia alone, each train carrying 440 tons.
Ref; Britains Military Airfields by David J Smith

22. *'HEINRICH HIMMLER'*, the evil head of the Nazi SS, was once a chicken farmer
Ref; as above

23. *'AKTION T4'*, was the code for the German Euthanesia programme to eliminate 'life unworthy of life' ie, the sick and disabled.
Ref; www.historyplace.com/worldwar2/timeline/euthanasia.htm

24. *'SAVAGE CHRISTIAN'*, was the nickname given to Christian Wirth, the high-ranking SS officer who headed the euthanasia programme responsible for *100,000 DEATHS.*

25. *'WHITE BREAD'*, was banned in Britain as from 11th March 1942

26. *'DOGS'* were trained by the Soviet Red Army to destroy enemy tanks. They were trained to associate the underside of tanks with food and were fitted with a 26lb explosive device strapped to their backs. Once the dogs crawled under the tanks, the device was triggered and exploded, destroying the tank (and of course, the dog). Unfortunately, this didn't always work as planned, as the dogs were trained using Russian tanks, so were more likely to run under these than the German tanks. As many as 25 German tanks were put out of

action this way, during the battles for Kursk and Stalingrad. There is no record of how many Russian tanks were blown up!
Source: Guiness Book of Records

27. 'MARGARINE' was first introduced in the French Navy in the 1890's. It was made from a substance extracted from cows udders and coloured an 'attractive' shade of light blue, then canned. It was discovered that, if the cans were not turned regularly, a layer of clear liquid rose to the surface. This 'organic' solvent was found to be an effective stain remover!
Ref; www.margarine.com

28. 'DEFINING MOMENT' in September 1918 at Marcoing, France. Private Henry Tandey V.C. was engaged in bitter hand to hand fighting. A wounded German soldier limped directly into his line of fire. "I took aim, but could not shoot a wounded man" said Tandey, "so I let him go". Years later, he discovered he'd spared an Austrian Corporal named Adolf Hitler.

Hitler never forgot that pivotal moment, or the man who'd spared him. On becoming German Chancellor in 1933, he ordered his staff to track down Tandey's service records. They also managed to obtain a print of an Italian painting showing Tandey carrying an injured Allied soldier on his back, which Hitler hung with pride on the wall at his mountain retreat at Berchtesgaden.

He showed the print to the British Prime Minister, Neville Chamberlain, during his historic visit in 1938 and explained it's significance.

Henry Tandey left the army before WW2 started and became a security guard in Coventry. His 'good deed' haunted him for the rest of his life, especially as German bombers almost destroyed Coventry in 1940 and London burned day and night during the Blitz. "If only I'd known what he'd turn out to be. When I saw all the people, women and children, he'd killed and wounded. I was sorry to God I let him go", he said before his death in 1977 at the age of 86.
Ref; The History Place-WW2statistics

29. 'SPAM' was a contraction of 'spiced ham'. It was introduced by the Hormel Meat Co. USA in 1936. It used up 'trimmings' of pork that

that could not otherwise be sold. It was pressed and canned and the tremendous need for wartime economics sent 'Spam' all over the world, where it became an essential part of Allied Forces battle rations. It was called many names, some of which are printable ie; 'mystery meat', 'ham that failed it's physical' etc. Despite the contempt by all Allied troops who were heartily sick of the stuff, 'Spam' became very popular after the war, especially in South Korea and the Phillipines.
Ref; www.spam.com

30. *'BISCUITS'*, There were only 20 varieties of biscuits manufactured in UK during the war.

31. *'YANKS IN BRITAIN'* were dubbed 'overpaid, overfed, oversexed and overhere'. The Americans responded by calling British servicemen, 'underpaid, underfed, undersexed and under Eisenhower. He being the Supreme Commander Allied Forces preparing for 'D' Day.

32. *'PETROL COST 5p per LITRE'*, but was rationed to 50 miles per week.

33. *'AVERAGE WARTIME WAGE FOR MEN'*, was £3.45p per Week

34. *'NEW SERVICEMAN'S PAY'*, was 70p per Week

35. *'WOJTEK'* was the name of a brown bear who helped to move boxes of ammunition for the 2nd Polish Corps in the battle of Monte Cassino
Ref; www.stokesey.demon.co.ukwwii/trivia

36. *'THE BOUNCING BOMB'* also known as **Highball**, used by the RAF to destroy German dams, was invented by Barnes Neville Wallace, who left school at 16 with **no qualifications** and worked in a shipyard. In 1913, he moved to Vickers to design airships and, much later, planes, including the very successful **Wellington bomber**. After the Dambusters raid, he went on and designed much